TETRAPYRROLE
BIOSYNTHESIS
AND ITS REGULATION

June Lascelles (*University of Oxford*): **Tetrapyrrole Biosynthesis and Its Regulation**

A. L. Lehninger (*The Johns Hopkins University*): **The Mitochondrion**

TETRAPYRROLE
BIOSYNTHESIS
AND ITS REGULATION

JUNE LASCELLES

Microbiology Unit

Department of Biochemistry

University of Oxford

W. A. BENJAMIN, INC.

New York   Amsterdam

1964

TETRAPYRROLE BIOSYNTHESIS AND ITS REGULATION

Library of Congress Catalog Card Number 64–22276
Manufactured in the United States of America

*The manuscript was put into production on 12 February 1964;
this volume was published on 28 August 1964*

*The publisher is pleased to acknowledge the assistance of
Carol Levine, who copyedited the manuscript, Ricky Ripp,
who produced the illustrations, and William Prokos, who
designed the cover and dust jacket*

W. A. BENJAMIN, INC.
One Park Avenue, New York, New York 10016

EDITOR'S FOREWORD

This book is the second to appear in a Series of Monographs in Microbial and Molecular Biology. The purpose of this series is to encourage and sponsor the publication of carefully selected and edited short monographs, of approximately 150 pages, on topics in the forefront of research in these fields.

Each book in the series will present a more comprehensive review of its topic, and a broader perspective, than is ordinarily possible in a review article. The presentations are intended to be sufficiently detailed, and thoroughly enough documented and illustrated, so that the advanced student will be able to obtain a comprehensive and up-to-date grasp of an actively developing area without having to refer extensively to original papers. To facilitate access to especially important experimental detail or theoretical development, reprints of key papers will at times be included.

These volumes are not primarily reference works, and they will differ from the traditional monograph in not necessarily covering every relevant reference. The rapid proliferation of the scientific literature makes it increasingly difficult for the experienced investigator, let alone the graduate student, to rely on his coverage of original articles to keep him informed of important advances across the general field of microbial and molecular biology. Hence the editor and the publisher believe that appropriate reviews are of increasing value; and for this purpose it seems to us more important that the reviews be critical and lucid than that they be exhaustive. Accordingly, we encourage the authors to be selective, to speculate on immediate problems and on directions of future advance, and to editorialize in much the same way as they would in lecturing to their own students.

I hope that this series of volumes will be of value to the scientific community. Criticisms and suggestions will be welcomed.

BERNARD D. DAVIS

Harvard Medical School
Boston, Massachusetts
March 1964

PREFACE

The tetrapyrrole structure is responsible for the color of hemoglobin and chlorophyll, the major pigments of living matter. The cytochromes, which also contain this structure, are just as important in living processes as the dominating pigments, though present in far lower concentration. It is not surprising, therefore, that the biosynthesis of tetrapyrroles has intrigued biochemists for the past twenty years, just as the elucidation of their chemical structure attracted organic chemists in the early part of this century.

Biochemists are greatly indebted to the monumental achievements of the chemists (in particular R. Willstätter and H. Fischer), which established that the major pigments of plants and animals, although green and red, respectively, were nevertheless built on the same tetrapyrrole structure. The magnitude of this work is emphasized if one considers that. it was done before the advent of modern chromatographic techniques and modern gadgets, such as recording spectrophotometers.

The complex tetrapyrrole structure is difficult to synthesize in the laboratory, yet most living cells can form it from simple precursors. Considerable progress toward a complete understanding of the biosynthetic pathway has been made within the last decade, and it has been shown that the same biosynthetic pathway operates in all forms of life.

The emphasis of research in this field has been mainly on heme synthesis in those animal tissues whose special function is to form hemoglobin. Important though this pigment is in the metabolism of higher animals, the major tetrapyrrole in living matter is chlorophyll and, since "all flesh is grass," animal life ultimately depends on the ability of plants to make chlorophyll and to use it to capture radiant energy. The path of chlorophyll synthesis has therefore a claim on the attention of biochemists equal to that of heme; consequently it has been considered in some detail in this monograph.

It is common now to find microorganisms being exploited in studies of biosynthesis because of their outstanding capabilities in this direction and because they can be grown in environments easily controlled by the experimenter. The contributions which these simple forms of life can make to investigations of tetrapyrrole biosynthesis have been realized only recently. Since the research interests of the writer have been confined to the biochemistry of microorganisms, it is not surprising to find that some emphasis has been given in this book to these humble creatures. No excuse is required for this self-indulgence, since some bacteria have a far higher capacity to form tetrapyrroles than the most active animal and plant tissues. In addition microorganisms offer unique opportunities for examination of mechanisms by which tetrapyrrole synthesis is regulated to ensure that the supply of these compounds is adequate for, but not in excess of, the metabolic requirements of the cell.

The main purpose of this monograph is to review the present status of the biosynthesis of heme and of chlorophyll and of how these processes are regulated. As background, chapters on the chemistry, distribution, and function of tetrapyrroles are included. These provide only a very superficial introduction to this large class of compounds; for more detailed and critical information the reader is directed to a number of excellent reviews. In dealing with the biosynthetic aspects the author has exercised a considerable amount of selection from the quite formidable amount of experimental material reported in the literature. The selection does not necessarily reflect any judgment of the value of the work, but is more a reflection of the writer's particular interests and limitations. In addition, aspects already reviewed in detail have been given less emphasis than less renowned aspects. The contention is that any form of life that can synthesize tetrapyrroles is of at least potential interest to the biochemist pursuing the biosynthesis of these substances; information gained with, for instance, a lowly microorganism might apply equally to more sophisticated creatures.

JUNE LASCELLES

Oxford, England
February 1964

ACKNOWLEDGMENTS

I am greatly indebted to my former colleague, Dr. B. F. Burnham, for reading the manuscript and for his advice and criticism. I am also grateful to Dr. R. J. Porra and Dr. J. Wittenberg for reading sections and making valuable suggestions. On the secretarial side, I am particularly indebted to Miss A. Pearce-Gervis for her care and skill which resulted in the production of an unblemished typescript from a tattered manuscript and to Miss P. Conibear for her help with the diagrams and bibliography.

J. L.

CONTENTS

xi

1

INTRODUCTION TO
TETRAPYRROLE STRUCTURES
AND THEIR PROPERTIES

The purpose of this chapter is to provide a background to the structure, nomenclature, and physical and chemical properties of tetrapyrroles and derivatives that are discussed from the biochemical point of view in subsequent chapters. This is merely a general introduction; a more thorough analysis of the chemistry of this class of compounds is given in the monographs of Lemberg and Legge (1949) and Falk (1964) and recent reviews by Granick and Mauzerall (1961), Falk (1963), and Phillips (1963).

1–1 TETRAPYRROLES AND DERIVATIVES:
STRUCTURE AND NOMENCLATURE

The tetrapyrroles are derivatives of porphin (Figure 1–1), which comprises four pyrrole rings (A, B, C, D) attached to each other through four methene bridges (α, β, γ, δ). The alternating single and double bonds of the inner 16-membered ring provide a resonating structure that is highly resistant to chemical attack. The resonating molecule has a flat structure, and all the resonating atoms lie on the same plane.

1

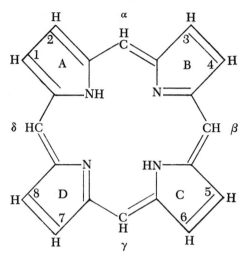

Figure 1–1   Porphin, showing the numbering of the tetrapyrrole structure.

The structures of the various tetrapyrroles found in nature are based on porphin modified in several ways:

1. by substitution of the outer β,β' C atoms (numbered 1 to 8) of the pyrrole rings; the substituent may be either an alkyl group or a hydrogen atom and an alkyl group as in the chlorophyll derivatives.

2. by the metal held in complex formation; such metal complexes may be further modified by valence changes, by the formation of coordination compounds and by combination with specific proteins.

3. by substitution or replacement of the methene bridge carbons. Substituents may be hydrogen atoms as in the porphyrinogens, or the cyclopentanone ring as in the chlorophylls. The corrin ring typical of vitamin B_{12} derivatives has lost the δ-methene bridge carbon.

One modification of the basic porphin structure of particular importance to the biochemist involves the reduction of the methene bridge carbons to methylene bridges. This addition of hydrogen to the methene carbons destroys the resonance of the 16-membered ring. The reduced compounds, designated porphyrinogens, no longer demonstrate the highly characteristic, visible absorption properties of porphyrins. Porphyrinogens are not planar molecules, and they are quite unstable to air oxidation.

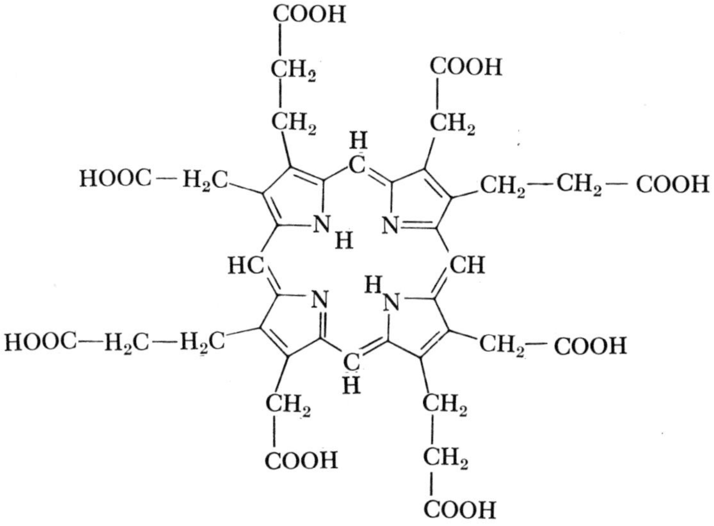

uroporphyrin I

Figure 1–2   Uroporphyrin I.

Porphyrins. The porphyrins are metal-free tetrapyrroles that are differentiated structurally by the nature and arrangement of the sidechains at the β positions of the pyrrole rings. For example, uroporphyrin has four acetic and four propionic acid sidechains (Figure 1–2). Since there are four theoretically possible arrangements of the acetic and propionic sidechains about the tetrapyrrole nucleus, there are four isomeric forms of uroporphyrin (types I, II, III, IV). Protoporphyrin, which has methyl, vinyl, and propionic acid sidechains, has 15 possible isomers, but only one, protoporphyrin IX, occurs naturally. In fact, nature seems to have chosen only one isomeric series, since all physiologically active tetrapyrroles have the same configuration as uroporphyrin III or protoporphyrin IX (subsequently referred to as protoporphyrin). The most common porphyrins are shown in Figure 1–3. Type I isomers of uro- and coproporphyrin have been isolated from natural materials, but these appear to have no physiological role and probably arise as a result of derangement in tetrapyrrole metabolism or of spontaneous chemical reactions of tetrapyrrole precursors.

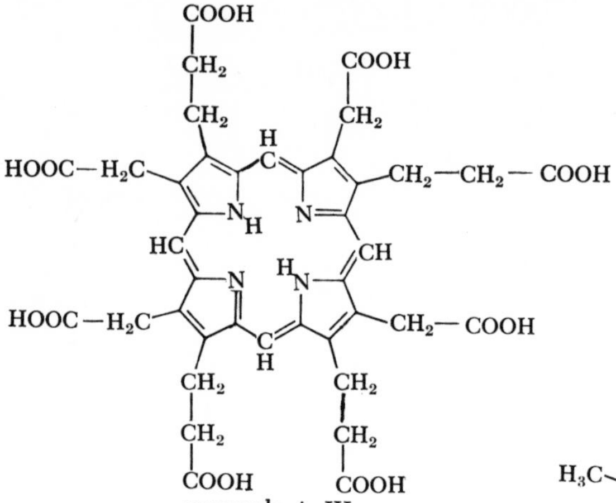

uroporphyrin III

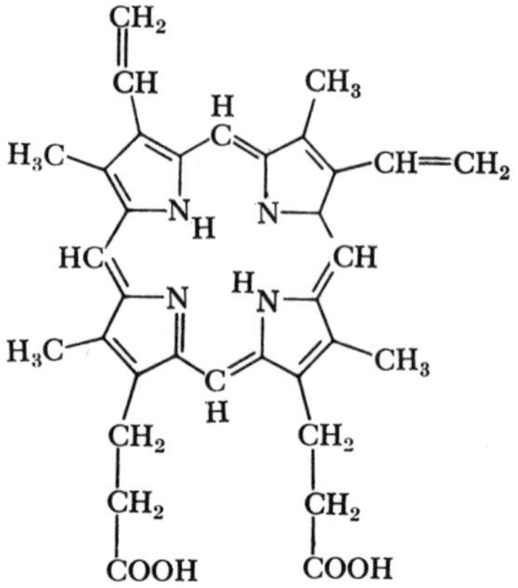

protoporphyrin IX

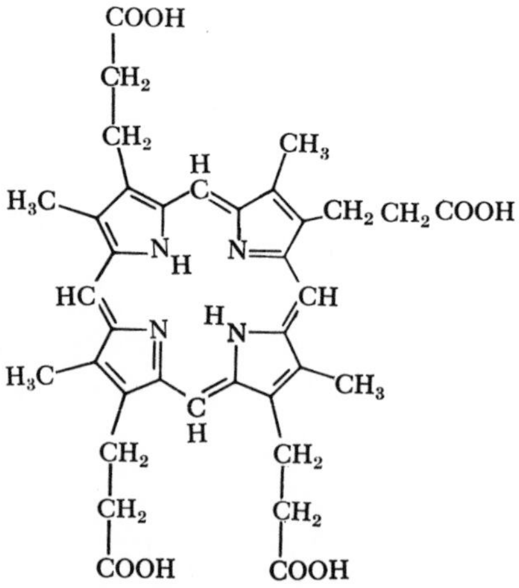

coproporphyrin III

Figure 1–3 Some naturally occurring porphyrins. Substitution of the vinyl sidechains of protoporphyrin with hydroxymethyl, ethyl, or hydrogen gives hemato-, meso-, and deuteroporphyrins, respectively.

Porphyrins are reduced to colorless porphyrinogens by treatment with sodium amalgam; these are intermediates in the biosynthesis of tetrapyrroles (Figure 1–4). They are oxidized spontaneously to porphyrins, the reoxidation being hastened by mild oxidizing agents such as iodine.

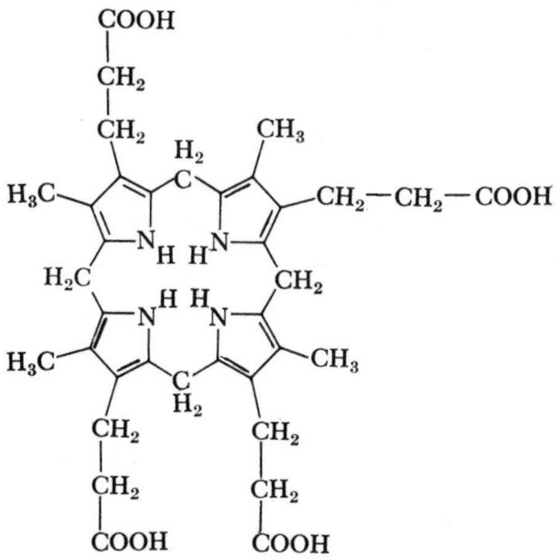

Figure 1–4 Coproporphyrinogen III.

Metalloporphyrins. Porphyrins readily combine with various metals to form chelates but only the ones with iron and magnesium have important biological roles. Complexes of uro- and coproporphyrin with copper, zinc, and manganese do occur in nature, for instance in urine; but they probably arise spontaneously, since these porphyrins tend to form chelates easily, especially under mildly alkaline conditions. Combination with metals occurs both with free porphyrins and with porphyrin esters (i.e., in the absence of carboxylic acid groups), and the metal complexes are soluble in organic solvents. These properties show that the metals are held in complex combination rather than as salts.

The iron complexes are known collectively as hemes, the nature of the porphyrin being specified by the appropriate prefix (e.g., coproheme). The most well-known is protoheme or iron protoporphyrin, in which the iron may be in the ferrous or ferric state. In general practice the terms heme and hematin refer to ferrous and ferric protoheme, respectively, and this terminology will be used throughout (see Figure 1–5). Heme, the prosthetic group of hemoglobin, is rapidly oxidized in contact with air to hematin or to hemin (ferric protoporphyrin chloride) if chloride ions are present. This chloride derivative, which is stable and the usual form in which the prosthetic group of hemoglobin is isolated, is most often used in biochemical studies.

Heme and Hematin Complexes. Heme has a planar structure imposed upon it by combination with protoporphyrin but two molecules or

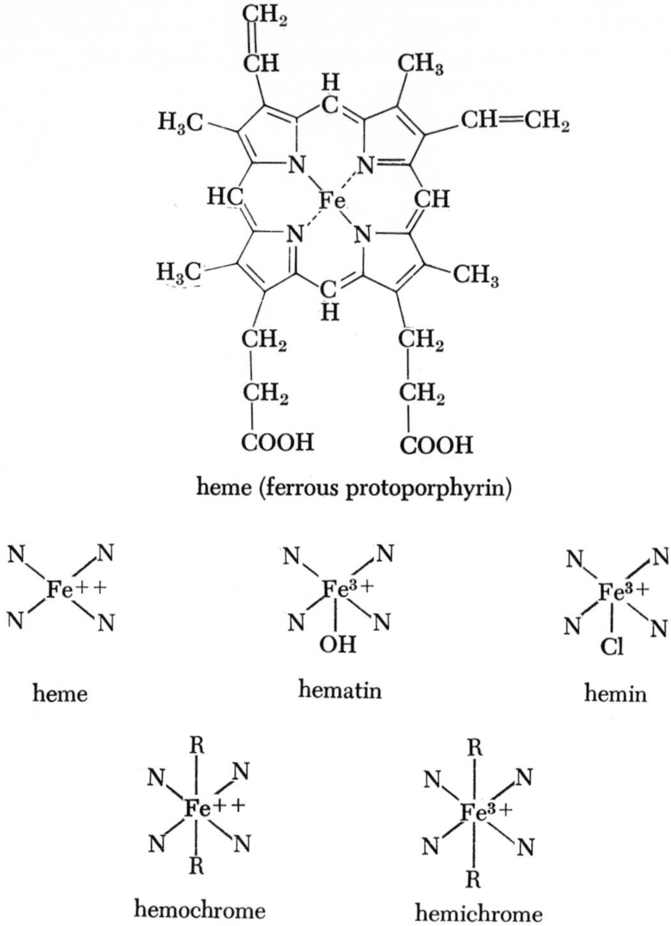

heme (ferrous protoporphyrin)

heme   hematin   hemin

hemochrome   hemichrome

Figure 1–5   Nomenclature of iron complexes of protoporphyrin.

ions may coordinate with the iron, one above and one below the plane of the porphyrin ring; these are *hemochromes* or *hemochromogens*. Coordinating substances include hydrogen peroxide, carbon monoxide, oxygen, cyanide ions, and nitrogenous bases such as pyridine and ammonia. Heme also combines with denatured proteins in which hemochrome-forming groups, such as the imidazole ring of histidine, are accessible. Hematin also forms similar complexes known as *hemichromes*. The iron in the hemichromes is in the ferric state; it is in the divalent state in hemochromes.

The proteins that have an iron porphyrin as prosthetic group are generally referred to as *hemoproteins;* this is a term of convenience and does not necessarily imply that the iron is in the reduced state or that the iron porphyrin is protoheme. The specific proteins are bound by coordination of the iron with suitable groups on amino acid residues, and additional covalent linkages may be formed between amino acid residues and sidechains of the porphyrin ring. The ease with which the iron porphyrin moiety is removed from the protein varies among the hemoproteins, depending on the presence and nature of the covalent bonds. In the absence of such bonds organic solvents may be effective; for instance heme is removed from hemoglobin at pH 2 with acetone without irreversible denaturation of the globin. With other hemoproteins, such as cytochrome *c*, hydrolysis with acid or alkali is required to break the covalent bonds. Full information about the linkage of protein to prosthetic group is so far available for very few hemoproteins.

Chlorophylls. The chlorophylls differ in structure from the hemes in four major respects (Figure 1–6): (1) They are complexes of magnesium; (2) ring D (plant chlorophylls) and rings D and B (bacteriochlorophyll) of the tetrapyrrole structure are in the fully reduced state; (3) they have an additional cyclopentanone ring (E) formed by cyclization of the propionic acid sidechain at C-6 with the γ methene C; and (4) the propionic sidechain at C-7 is esterified with a long-chain isoprenoid alcohol, usually phytol.

There are at least eight different types of chlorophyll in nature (Aronoff, 1960; Bogorad, 1962; Hill, 1963; Smith and French, 1963). Chlorophyll *a* and *b* and bacteriochlorophyll are the most well-known forms (Figure 1–6). Other types of chlorophyll (chlorophyll *c*, *d* and *e*, Chlorobium chlorophyll 650 and 660) found in some species of algae and in the green sulfur bacteria differ from the well-recognized forms in their absorption spectrum but knowledge of their structure is as yet incomplete. In some cases the differences from chlorophyll *a* or *b* may be relatively slight; for instance, chlorophyll *d* is probably 2-formyl chlorophyll *a* (Holt and Morley, 1959). The Chlorobium chlorophylls 650 and 660 appear to differ fundamentally from all other known forms in that they lack the methoxyl group esterified with the carboxyl group at C-10 (Holt, Hughes, Kende, and Purdie, 1962; 1963). Also, the isoprenoid sidechain is not phytol ($C_{20}H_{39}OH$) but is probably *trans-trans*-farnesol ($C_{15}H_{25}OH$) (Rapoport and Hamlow, 1961).

The nomenclature of chlorophyll derivatives is based upon the

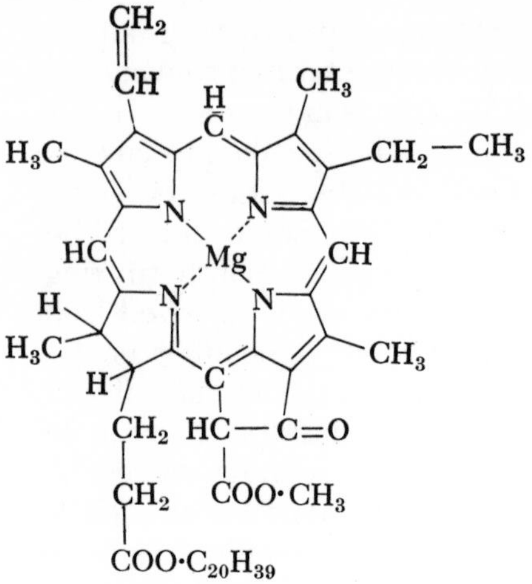

chlorophyll *a*

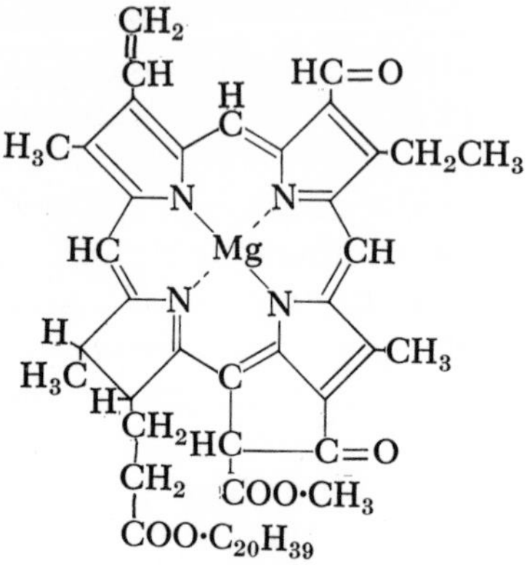

chlorophyll *b*

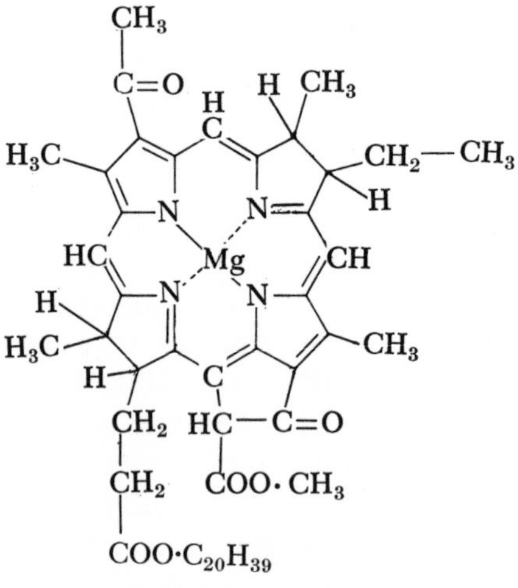

bacteriochlorophyll

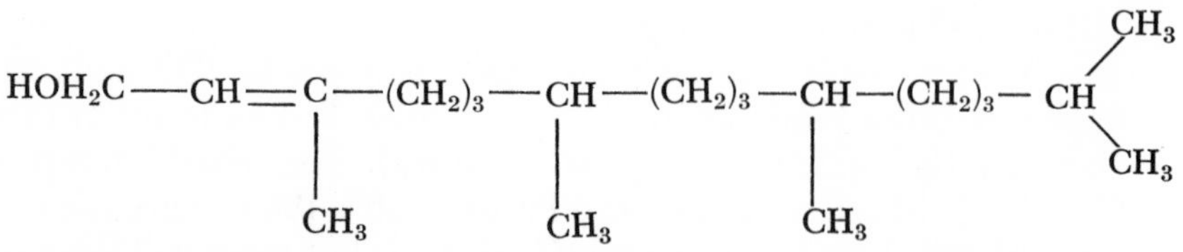

phytol

Figure 1–6   Chlorophyll *a, b*, bacteriochlorophyll, and phytol.

Table 1–1   Derivatives*a* of chlorophyll *a*

Name	Magnesium	Phytol
Chlorophyll *a*	+	+
Chlorophyllide *a*	+	−
Pheophytin *a*	−	+
Pheophorbide *a*	−	−

a The derivatives differ from chlorophyll *a* only in respect to the magnesium and the phytol.

presence or absence of magnesium and of the phytol group. Those of chlorophyll *a* that appear most frequently in this monograph are shown in Table 1–1. Corresponding derivatives of bacterio-chlorophyll are prefixed by "bacterio" (e.g., bacteriopheophytin).

All chlorophylls in vivo are bound to lipoprotein complexes but linkage nature is unknown. Since they may be readily extracted with organic solvents, strong covalent bonds are not indicated.

Open-Chain Tetrapyrroles. These highly colored compounds occur in nature mainly as the bile pigments and as the prosthetic groups of the phycobilins of the red and blue-green algae. There is a be-wildering variety of bile pigments differing in the degree of hydro-genation of the C atoms linking the pyrrole rings (Gray, 1961). Since the open-chain compounds lack the stable resonance struc-ture of the porphyrin nucleus, they are unstable and readily un-dergo oxidation. The type and distribution of the aliphatic side-chains are like protoporphyrin except that some have ethyl in place of vinyl groups.

The phycobilins of the red and blue-green algae are water soluble chromoproteins with bile pigments as prosthetic groups (ÓhEocha, 1962). There are at least two types of phycobilin, phycocyanin (blue) and phycoerythrin (red). The probable struc-

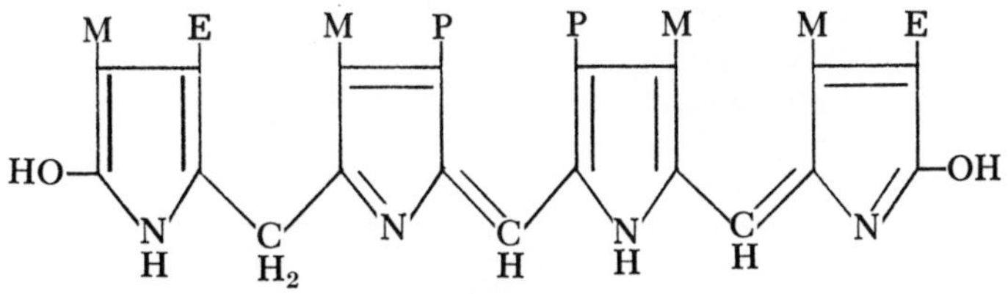

Figure 1–7   Phycocyanobilin.

ture of the chromophore of phycocyanin (phycocyanobilin) is shown in Figure 1–7; that of phycoerythrin (phycoerythrobilin) is probably slightly more reduced.

1–2 PHYSICAL PROPERTIES OF TETRAPYRROLES

Solubility. The comparatively large, planar, aromatic cyclic tetra-pyrrole nucleus is predominantly hydrophobic. This characteristic is modified by the presence of aliphatic sidechains with hydro-philic alcoholic and carboxylic acid groups. Ether and dioxane are commonly used organic solvents for tetrapyrroles; many of the chlorophylls with their long-chain phytol group are also soluble in petroleum ether. Porphyrins and their metal complexes are readily soluble in acidified organic solvents, e.g., acetone-HCl, ether- or ethyl acetate-acetic acid.

The solubility of tetrapyrroles in aqueous dilute acid or alkali depends on the number of free carboxylic acid groups; of the common, naturally occurring porphyrins, uroporphyrin is the most and protoporphyrin the least soluble. Partition between ether and hydrochloric acid is the basis of a classical method for the separation and identification of porphyrins and derivatives (Willstätter and Mieg, 1913). In this method the compounds in ether solution are successively extracted with aqueous hydrochloric acid of increasing concentration. The *HCl number*, a characteristic physical constant of porphyrins, is defined as the per cent HCl that extracts two-thirds of the porphyrin from water-saturated ether into an equal volume of aqueous layer. The HCl numbers of some tetrapyrroles and derivatives are given in Table 1–2.

Table 1–2   HCl numbers of some tetrapyrroles and derivatives[a]

	HCl number	
Compound	Free	Methyl ester
Uroporphyrin I	[b]	7
Coproporphyrin III	0.09	1.5
Hematoporphyrin	0.1	
Protoporphyrin	2.0	5.5
Pheophorbide *a*	15	
Pheophytin *a*	29	

[a] The values are taken from the review by Granick and Gilder (1947).
[b] Uroporphyrin is not soluble in ether.

Besides free carboxylic acid groups the presence of alcoholic groups also influences the HCl number; hence hematoporphyrin with two alcoholic groups besides two carboxylic acid groups has a lower HCl number than protoporphyrin. Esterification of the carboxylic acid groups increases the HCl number. The highest numbers are found with chlorophyll derivatives, particularly when the molecule is phytylated.

Absorption Spectra. The conjugated double bond system of the porphyrin nucleus is a chromophore that provides strong and characteristic absorption bands in the near ultraviolet and visible regions of the spectrum. The absorption spectra of the tetrapyrroles are of prime importance in their identification and estimation. All compounds in this group exhibit maximum absorption in the region 350 to 450 mμ, the Soret band. The number and pattern of the bands in the visible region vary with the type of tetrapyrrole, the solvent and pH (Figure 1–8).

The porphyrins in organic solvents or weak alkali show a typical four-banded spectrum in the visible region the intensity of the bands increasing regularly from the red (α band) to the blue end of the spectrum. Under these conditions solutions of porphyrin are red-brown in color. The sidechains on the pyrrole rings do not influence the pattern or relative intensity of the bands, but they do affect their position and absolute intensity and are therefore a good guide to the identification of porphyrins (Table 1–3). In acid solution porphyrins are colored purple-red and the four-banded "neutral" spectrum is replaced by a sharp two-banded one with a weak third band between them; the Soret band is also intensified. Divalent metal porphyrins have a two-banded visible spectrum similar to an acid porphyrin but in the latter the bands are displaced more to the red.

Hemochromes also have a two-banded spectrum with a sharp maximum (the α band) at 550 to 560 mμ; this band is particularly

Table 1–3   Absorption maxima of porphyrins at alkaline pH[a]

	Position of bands, mμ			
Porphyrin	α	β	γ	δ
Uroporphyrin	612	560.5	539	504
Coproporphyrin	617.5	565.5	538.5	503
Protoporphyrin	642	591	540	Indistinct

[a] Values are for the porphyrins in 0.1 N KOH (Schumm, 1927).

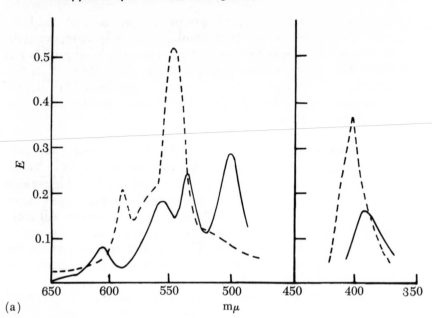

(a)

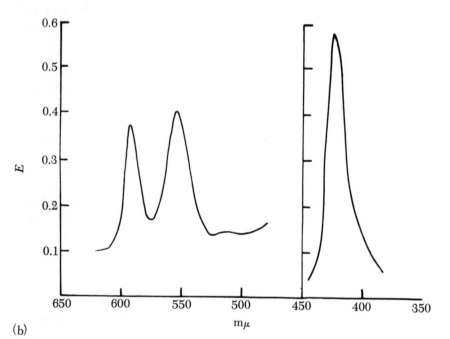

(b)

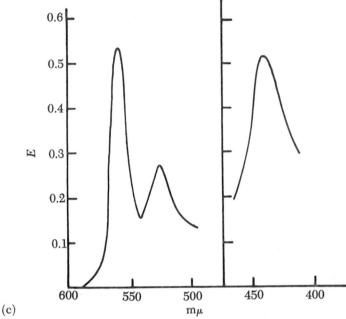

(c)

Figure 1–8   Absorption spectra of porphyrins and metal complexes. (a) Coproporphyrin III in 0.02 N NaOH (solid) or 0.15 N HCl (dashed); the concentration is 30 and 1.8 μM for the visible and Soret regions, respectively. (b) Mg-protoporphyrin in 0.01 N NaOH; the concentration is 18 (visible) and 1.8 μM (Soret). (c) Iron protoporphyrin pyridine hemochrome in 0.02 N NaOH; the concentration is 17 (visible) and 4 μM (Soret).

important in the identification and estimation of heme compounds including the cytochromes.

The dihydro- and tetrahydro-ring system of the chlorophylls results in a characteristic intense absorption at the long wavelengths (Figure 1–9). Dihydroporphyrins in organic solvents have a prominent band at about 660 mμ with other relatively minor bands in the visible region. The tetrahydro-ring structure of bacteriochlorophyll shifts the position of the α band far into the red to about 770 mμ in organic solvents. In both plants and bacteria the absorption maxima of the chlorophylls in vivo differ from those of the extracted pigments in organic solvents, and are shifted further into the red; the shift is about 100 mμ in the case of bacteriochlorophyll (Figure 1–9) (French, 1960). Other peaks in the red are also evident in the spectra of the bacteria. The reasons for the dif-

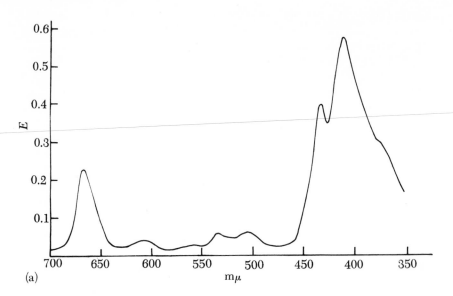

(a)

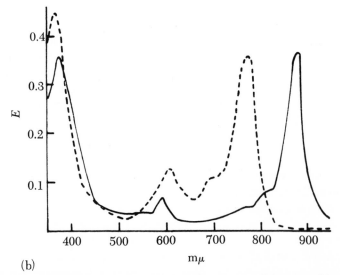

(b)

Figure 1–9   Absorption spectra of pheophytin *a* and bacteriochlorophyll.
(*a*) Pheophytin *a* in ether (3 μM). (*b*) Bacteriochlorophyll in whole
cells of *R. spheroides* carotenoidless mutant (solid) and in ether
(dashed; 4 μM). From Stanier and Cohen-Bazire (1957).

ferences in in vivo and in vitro spectra are not fully understood but they are probably caused by binding and interaction of the pigments with the subcellular structures in which they are located.

The open-chain tetrapyrroles absorb strongly in the visible region showing a variety of absorption maxima between 400 and 650 mμ depending on the compound; in contrast to the cyclic tetrapyrroles, they lack the Soret band.

Fluorescence. A characteristic property of free porphyrins is the intense red fluorescence emitted on irradiation with ultraviolet light at wavelengths of about 400 mμ. Porphyrins present in amounts as low as 1 part in 100,000 can be detected in this way and fluorometric methods have been used for their estimation. The intensity of the fluorescence is influenced by the pH, being minimal at the isoelectric point and more pronounced in mineral acid at about pH 1. Some of the porphyrin metal complexes also fluoresce, although less intensely than the free porphyrins. The same property is exhibited by the chlorophylls and their derivatives and has been the subject of considerable study in view of its possible connection with the mechanism of photosynthesis.

1–3 ISOLATION AND IDENTIFICATION

The isolation and identification by chromatography of the porphyrins and their metal complexes have been fully reviewed by Falk (1961) and of the chlorophylls and derivatives by Šesták (1958). The following summarizes the methods in most general use.

Porphyrins and Metal Complexes. Porphyrins may be extracted quantitatively from natural materials with acidified organic solvents such as acetone-HCl, ethyl acetate, or ether-glacial acetic acid. These methods are also effective in splitting the heme moiety from hemoproteins except those bound by covalent bonds, such as cytochrome c, where more drastic procedures are necessary (Paul, 1960). After removal of the acid by washing with sodium acetate, porphyrins in the organic phase are removed by extraction with increasing concentrations of HCl. The hemes, which are not soluble in acid, remain in the solvent phase. At this stage further identification and estimation by measurement of the absorption spectra can be made.

Several chromatographic procedures are available for separating porphyrins and their metal complexes. On the preparative scale, chromatography on columns of alumina, magnesium oxide, and calcium carbonate has been extensively used to purify porphyrins as their methyl esters. Hemes have been separated on silicic acid or silica gel columns. In the column methods the developing solvents include benzene, chloroform, and methanol. With paper chromatographic methods for separating porphyrins, aqueous lutidine mixtures have been proved most useful, the R_F of the porphyrins bearing a linear relation to the number of carboxylic acid chains on the molecule. Separation of the four isomers of coproporphyrin can also be achieved in this solvent system. More extensive separation of the isomeric porphyrins (as their methyl esters) occurs in mixtures of chloroform-kerosene and propanol-kerosene. Hemes or their methyl esters may also be separated in reverse-phase systems using silicone impregnated paper with aqueous solvent mixtures.

Chlorophylls and Derivatives. The chlorophylls are bound within cells to lipoprotein complexes, but these are split readily by extraction with aqueous polar solvents such as acetone and methanol. When separated from cell structures they are easily soluble in pure organic solvents. Bacteriochlorophyll is unstable in this form and solutions must be protected from the light; the plant chlorophylls are less labile.

Many column chromatographic procedures are available for freeing extracted chlorophylls from contaminating carotenoids and other lipids, as well as for separating the individual forms of chlorophyll (Smith and Benitez, 1955). Powdered sucrose is a common adsorbent and development may be achieved with mixtures of nonpolar and polar solvents such as light petroleum and methanol. Recently an improved method using columns of powdered polyethylene has been described (Anderson and Calvin, 1962). Numerous paper chromatographic methods for separation have been described with similar solvent mixtures. Differentiation between phytylated and nonphytylated chlorophyll derivatives, which cannot be made spectrophotometrically, is easily made by chromatography, since the phytol moiety confers greater solubility in nonpolar solvents such as light petroleum or benzene.

Chlorophylls are usually estimated by measurement of the extinction at the maximum at the long red wavelength, about 660 mμ in the case of chlorophyll a and 770 mμ for bacteriochlorophyll. At these wavelengths interference by other pigments does not occur.

2

DISTRIBUTION AND FUNCTION
OF TETRAPYRROLES

Tetrapyrroles in the form of hemoproteins and chlorophylls are found in most forms of life, ranging from unicellular microorganisms to the higher animals. The only exceptions appear to be some of the strictly anaerobic bacteria and lactobacilli, which obtain energy by fermentation of organic substrates. These tetrapyrrole derivatives function primarily in energy metabolism, as carriers of oxygen (the hemoglobins), as electron carriers (the cytochromes), or as agents for trapping radiant energy (the chlorophylls).

2–1 HEMOGLOBIN

Lemberg and Legge (1949) have defined the hemoglobins as a class of ferrous porphyrin proteins able to combine reversibly with oxygen without oxidation of the iron to the ferric state. In multicellular, highly differentiated organisms that depend on oxygen as terminal H-acceptor, a mechanism is required to ferry atmospheric oxygen from the oxygen-absorbing centers (e.g., lung) to the tissues not directly in contact with the atmosphere. The hemoglobins fulfil this role of oxygen carrier, the oxygen bound reversibly to the iron porphyrin moiety by coordinate bonds.

Table 2–1   Hemoglobin, myoglobin, and cytochrome c in higher animals[a]

Species	Body mass, kg	Hemoglobin, g	Myoglobin, g	Cytochrome c, g
Dog	9.88	138.3	7.5	0.249
		(8.1)	(0.44)	(0.021)
Man	70.0	912.8	34.7	0.781
		(54.0)	(2.1)	(0.065)
Horse	500.0	5805.5	1867.5	16.6
		(342)	(110)	(1.4)

[a] Data from Drabkin (1951). The values for the heme component are given in parentheses and are expressed as mmoles; they have been calculated on the assumption of 1 mole of heme per 17,000 g of hemoglobin and of myoglobin and one mole of heme c per 12,000 g of cytochrome c.

Hemoglobins in Animal Tissues

Vertebrates. The hemoglobin in the red blood cells of all vertebrates (*true hemoglobin*) has been the most intensively studied both in purified form and in vivo in normal and pathological states. There is a vast literature on this hemoprotein, so it receives only passing mention here (Lemberg and Legge, 1949; Galton, 1959; Wintrobe, 1961; Schroeder, 1963; Hayaishi, 1963). Hemoglobin has a molecular weight of 68,000 and contains 4 moles of heme per mole of the basic protein, globin. The globin moiety varies with the species of animal but in all heme is the prosthetic group. The red muscle of vertebrates contains another from of hemoglobin, myoglobin, with a molecular weight of 17,500 and containing one heme molecule per molecule of protein. The determination of the complete structure of human hemoglobin and of whale myoglobin is one of the outstanding achievements of this decade (Perutz, 1962).

Hemoglobin is by far the major tetrapyrrole-containing substance in vertebrate tissues, being present in human blood at a concentration of about 145 mg/ml of whole blood, equivalent to 5.2 mg of heme (Table 2–1). The concentration of myoglobin in tissues is far lower than that of hemoglobin; in man, for instance, it is present at about one-twentieth the amount of blood pigment (Drabkin, 1951).

Invertebrates. The blood of many invertebrates contains oxygen-carrying hemoproteins, which differ from vertebrate hemoglobin in that the protein moiety has a molecular weight of up to three million. In some species these occur in blood corpuscles and in others they are dissolved in the hemolymph. The erythrocruorins are the most widely distributed of these pigments and have heme as prosthetic group (Rimington and Kennedy, 1962). The hemolymph of some polychaete worms contains chlorocruorin, a green hemoprotein of high molecular weight, whose prosthetic group differs from heme in having a formyl in place of the vinyl group of C-2 of the porphin ring (*Spirographis* or chlorocruoro-heme).

Maintenance of hemoglobin in the reduced state. Hemoglobin functions in vivo at oxygen tensions that are suitable for its conversion to methemoglobin in which the iron is in the ferric form. Methemoglobin does not combine with oxygen and is therefore physiologically inactive. In the normal red blood cell the methemoglobin concentration is low (0.5 g/100 ml of packed red cells to be compared with 33.5 g of hemoglobin). The methemoglobin level is raised in some pathological states; this may be induced by drugs such as sulfonamides. Nitrite oxidizes hemoglobin to the ferric state and its accumulation in the blood is responsible for nitrate toxicity in cattle; rumen bacteria reduce ingested nitrate to nitrite, which is then absorbed into the blood stream (Wang, Garcia-Rivera, and Burris, 1961).

Since under normal conditions the methemoglobin level is low, the red blood cell must have reducing mechanisms for maintaining the iron in the reduced form in spite of the presence of oxygen. Glutathione, which is present in relatively high concentration in red cells, may function in this capacity, since it readily reduces methemoglobin. A specific enzyme, methemoglobin reductase, has also been postulated and a protein fraction with this activity has been isolated from red blood cells (Huennekens and Gabrio, 1954). Methemoglobin is, however, readily converted to the ferrous state by reduced flavins and it has been suggested that any flavoprotein with a readily dissociable prosthetic group could serve as a methemoglobin reductase (Cormier and Rostorfer, 1956).

Hemoglobins Associated with Microorganisms

Fungi and protozoa. Hemoproteins with the properties of hemoglobins as defined by Lemberg and Legge have been detected spectroscopically in some samples of bakers' yeast (*Saccharocymes cerevisiae*), in the molds *Neurospora crassa* and *Penicillium notatum,* and in the protoza *Tetrahymena pyriformis* and *Paramecium caudatum* (Keilin, 1953; Keilin and Tissières, 1953; Keilin and Ryley, 1953). These pigments are detectable in strongly aerated

Table 2–2   Hemoglobin concentration in microorganisms and root nodules[a]

Source	Hemoglobin heme	Total heme	Reference
N. crassa	0.012	0.02	Keilin and Tissières (1953)
P. caudatum	0.85	1.52	
			Keilin and Ryley (1953)
T. pyriformis	0.18	0.46	
Soy bean nodules			
Effective	0.11	0.12	
			Smith (1949a)
Ineffective	0.01	0.013	

[a] The values are as μmoles of heme per g fresh weight except for P. caudatum and T. pyriformis, which are per g dry weight. They have been calculated from the mean values given in the literature.

suspensions and exhibit absorption bands at 583 and 545 mμ. They combine with carbon monoxide to give compounds with maxima at 574 and 539 mμ and are oxidized by ferricyanide to give the weak spectrum characteristic of methemoglobin. Paramecium hemoglobin has been isolated and shown to have properties similar in many respects to that of mammalian myoglobin, although its molecular weight is significantly lower (13,000) and it has an exceptionally high affinity for oxygen (Smith, George, and Preer, 1962).

These hemoproteins contribute 30 to 50 per cent of the total hemes of the organisms (Table 2–2). Their function, if any, is not known. Possibly they might be merely byproducts formed during the biosynthesis of the cytochromes and their ability to combine with oxygen might have no biological significance. Another possibility is that the pigments are a rudiment of the evolutionary development of hemoglobin in higher organisms.

Root nodules. The red pigment (leghemoglobin; legoglobin), which is clearly evident in active root nodules of leguminous plants, was identified as hemoglobin by Keilin and Wang (1945) by observations similar to those described above. The pigment has recently been crystallized and some of its properties described (Ellfolk, 1960; Appleby, 1962).

This hemoprotein is confined to the nodule cells that contain the bacteroids, i.e., the form taken by the symbiotic nitrogen-fixing bacteria of the Rhizobium species after invasion of the root tissue.

It comprises the major proportion of the total hemes in these tissues (Keilin and Smith, 1947; Smith, 1949b; see Table 2–2). Electron microscopy has shown that the infecting bacteria are enclosed within a membrane envelope and the hemoglobin is presumed to be in solution within this envelope (Bergersen and Briggs, 1958; Bergersen, 1960).

There is strong circumstantial evidence for the association of this pigment with symbiotic nitrogen fixation that may be summarized as follows (Smith, 1949a):

1. It is present in nodules of all leguminous plants that actively fix nitrogen.

2. It is not present in nodules produced by ineffective strains of *Rhizobia* (Table 2–2).

3. Symbiotic nitrogen fixation is inhibited by carbon monoxide at concentrations much lower than those required to inhibit fixation by the free-living nitrogen fixers, *Azotobacter* and *Nostoc* spp.

It was first thought to be an oxygen store or carrier for respiration of the nodule but this seems unlikely for several reasons (Smith, 1949b). The concentration of hemoglobin is sufficient to support respiration for only about 3 minutes, and carbon monoxide at concentrations sufficient to saturate the pigment does not affect the Q_{O_2} of nodules although nitrogen fixation is inhibited. Also, the Q_{O_2} of ineffective nodules lacking the pigment is similar to that of effective nodules. Recent work has provided evidence that the hemoprotein may play a direct role in electron transport involved in the reduction of nitrogen gas to ammonia. Spectroscopic observations of nodule extracts have shown that the iron of the hemoglobin is oxidized to the ferric state when the atmosphere is changed from helium to nitrogen; this change is reversible, the oxidized pigment being restored to the reduced state on return to a helium atmosphere (Hamilton, Shug, and Wilson, 1957; Bergersen and Wilson, 1959). Preparations of the bacteroids washed free of nodule tissue are also able to reduce the oxidized pigment in a helium atmosphere. A working hypothesis on the mechanism of symbiotic nitrogen fixation has been proposed by Bergersen (1960) on the basis of these spectroscopic observations coupled with the finding that N^{15} is incorporated primarily into the membrane envelope enclosing the bacteroids in the nodules. The bacteroid membrane complex is suggested as responsible for reduction of the nitrogen gas to ammonia by means of a coupled electron transport chain that includes the hemoglobin as a component. Another possibility, which accords with the experimental observations and with the properties of the pigment, is that a direct combination may occur between it and a free radical that could be a primary intermediate in the fixation mechanism (Abel, Bauer, and Spence, 1963).

Clearly, considerably more information is required before the function of leghemoglobin can be established. It is particularly important, for instance, to demonstrate that ammonia formation is associated with the oxidation by gaseous nitrogen of the hemoglobin iron.

2-2 CYTOCHROMES

The most widely distributed of the hemoproteins are the cytochromes, which are intracellular pigments showing marked absorption in the visible region of the spectrum (Dixon and Webb, 1964; Morton, 1958; Paul, 1960; Falk, Lemberg, and Morton, 1961). The function of many of the cytochromes observed in various organisms is not yet definitely established but they all appear to act as electron carriers, the iron of the prosthetic group undergoing reduction and oxidation. Some, such as the cytochrome oxidases, have enzymic activity; whereas others may act only as electron carriers.

Types of Cytochrome and their Prosthetic Groups. There are three major groups of cytochromes, *a, b,* and *c,* each containing a different iron porphyrin prosthetic group (Figure 2–1). The structure of heme *a* has recently been established; particularly noteworthy is the alkyl substituent built up from isoprene units (Grassl, Coy, Seyffert, and Lynen, 1963). Cytochromes of the *b* group have iron protoporphyrin as prosthetic group. Those of the *c* group have a covalently-bound prosthetic group in which two cystein groups of the protein are linked to the double bonds of the vinyl sidechains to form thioether linkages of great stability. A fourth group of cytochromes, a_2, has been found so far only in some bacterial species. The prosthetic group (heme a_2) is green and is a dihydroporphyrin derivative, probably having ring D in the reduced form as in chlorophyll *a.* The complete structure is still unknown but, like heme *a,* it has alkyl substituent(s) although it lacks a formyl group (Barrett, 1956; Lemberg, Clezy, and Barrett, 1961). Several bacterial cytochromes are known to have two hemes per molecule (Newton and Kamen, 1961), but the cytochrome oxidase purified from *Pseudomonas aeruginosa* is apparently unique in that the prosthetic

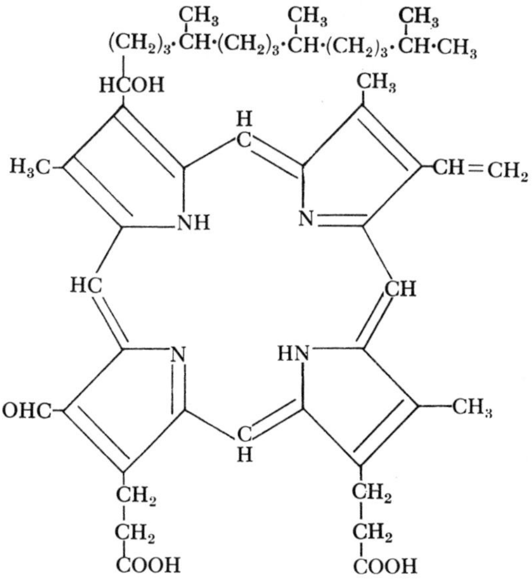

porphyrin *a*

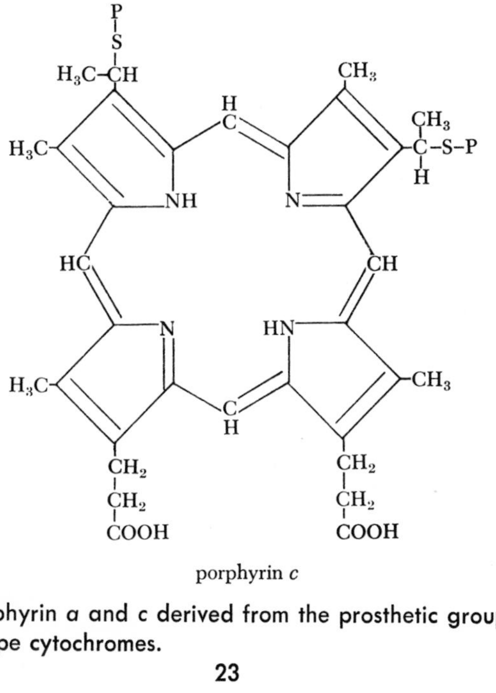

porphyrin *c*

Figure 2–1   Porphyrin *a* and *c* derived from the prosthetic groups of *a*- and *c*-type cytochromes.

23

groups are different, one being heme a_2 and the other heme c (Yamanaka and Okunuki, 1963).

The different prosthetic groups of the cytochromes (in combination with the specific protein) impose characteristic absorption spectra, and the various categories can be recognized by the position of the α-absorption band of the reduced pigment and of the pyridine hemochrome derivatives. Differentiation of the cytochromes within a group is based mainly on the precise position of the α-absorption band of the reduced form and by their behavior with respiratory inhibitors such as cyanide, carbon monoxide, and azide.

Distribution and Localization. A bewildering variety of cytochromes has been observed in animals, plants, and microorganisms but relatively few have been isolated in the pure state. Table 2–3 gives examples of cytochromes found in a variety of species. Apart from their universal distribution it is notable that the attachment of the

Table 2–3   Distribution and characteristics of some cytochromes[a]

Cyto-chrome	Prosthetic group	Found in	Position of α band, reduced, $m\mu$	E_0', volt pH 7.0,
a	Heme a	Heart muscle mitochondria,[1]	605	+0.29
a_3	Heme a	yeast, some bacteria, plants		
a_2	Heme a_2	*Aerobacter aerogenes* and other bacteria[2]	645	
b	Protoheme	Heart muscle mitochondria[3] (plants, some bacteria)	562	+0.05
b_1	Protoheme	*Corynebacterium diphtheriae* and other bacteria[4]	560	<+0.2
b_2	Protoheme	*Saccharomyces cerevisiae* (yeast)	557	
c	Heme c	Heart muscle mitochondria,	550	+0.255
c_1	Heme c	Yeast, plants, some bacteria	553–554	
c_3	Heme c	*Desulphovibrio desulphuricans*[5]	553	−0.205
c_5	Heme c	*Azotobacter vinelandii*	555	+0.32
f	Heme c	Chloroplasts	555	+0.365
RHP	Heme c	*Rhodospirillum rubrum*[6]	547 and 565	+0.008

[a] The information is from the review by Morton (1958) or from the following: (1) Griffiths and Wharton, 1961; (2) Barrett, 1956; (3) Goldberger et al., 1961; (4) Pappenheimer, 1955; (5) Postgate, 1956; (6) Kamen and Bartsch, 1961.

respective iron porphyrin to the various proteins results in a considerable range of redox potentials (from −0.205 to + 0.37 volt).

Cytochrome systems are predominantly located in the cell structures associated with phosphorylation coupled to electron transport. The difficulties encountered in isolating many of the cytochromes are attributable to their being bound to these multienzyme complexes, which are rich in lipoprotein. In animal cells they are found in the mitochondria, and the studies of D. E. Green's laboratory have contributed in particular to their isolation and to an understanding of their function in electron transport in these cell organelles (Green, 1963). The cytochromes are also present in the plant mitochondria; the chloroplasts are rich in specific cytochromes (for example, cytochrome f), which probably play a key role in photosynthetic phosphorylation (Hill and Scarisbrick, 1951; Arnon, 1963; Kamen, 1963). Bacterial cytochromes are mainly con-

Table 2–4   Concentration of cytochromes in various tissues[a]

Material	Values expressed as mg per	Cytochromes, μm-moles	Reference
Rat liver	dry wt	0.05 (c)	(1)
Rat heart	dry wt	0.16 (c)	(1)
Beef liver mitochondria	protein	1.3 (a)	(2)
(electron transport particle)	protein	0.68 (b)	
	protein	0.60 $(c + c_1)$	
Elder leaf	fresh wt	0.009 (f)	(3)
Yeast (Saccharomyces cerevisiae; aerobic)	dry wt	0.15 (c)	(4)
Neurospora crassa	dry wt	0.16 (c)	(5)
Azotobacter vinelandii	protein	0.54 $(c_4 + c_5)$	(6)
Aerobacter aerogenes	dry wt	0.033 (a_2)	(7)
	dry wt	0.31 (b_1)	
Rhodospirillum rubrum	dry wt	0.11 (c_2)	(8)
(photosynthetically grown)	dry wt	0.069 (b)	
	dry wt	0.085 (RHP)	
Desulphovibrio desulphuricans	dry wt	0.097 (c_3)	(9)
Vibrio succinogenes (nitrate-grown)	protein	0.55 (b_1)	(10)
		2.4 (c)	

[a] Values have been calculated from the data in the following references: (1) Drabkin, 1951; (2) Green, 1963; (3) Davenport and Hill, 1952; (4) Ephrussi, 1952; (5) Tissières and Mitchell, 1954; (6) personal observations of the author; (7) Barrett, 1956; (8) Clayton, 1959; Geller, 1962; (9) Postgate, 1961; (10) Jacobs and Wolin, 1963a.

Table 2–5   Concentration of chlorophyll and total hemes in photosynthetic tissues[a]

Source	Values expressed per	Total		
		Chlorophyll	Hemes	Reference
Higher plants and algae				
Triticum vulgare (leaf)	mg fresh wt	3.7	0.052	(1)
Euglena gracilis	mg protein	22		(2)
Scenedesmus	mg protein	20		(2)
Bacteria				
Rsp. rubrum	mg dry wt	22	0.43	(2)
Rps. spheroides	mg dry wt	27	0.29	(2)
Chromatium	mg dry wt	24	0.42	(2)
Bacterial chromatophores				
Rps. spheroides	mg protein	117	3.1	(3)
Chromatium	mg protein	155	7	(4)
Chlor. thiosulfatophilum	mg protein	98	0.67	(4)

[a] Values are in μm-moles. The analyses were made with cultures growing under normal conditions at medium light intensity; variation in the chlorophyll content occurs in different environments. References: (1) Hill and Scarisbrick, 1951; (2) unpublished personal observations; (3) Gibson, Neuberger, and Tait, 1962; (4) Hulcher and Conti, 1960.

fined to the particulate fraction of the cell together with other components of the electron transport chain (Bruemmer et al., 1957; Smith, 1961). This fraction arises by fragmentation of the cell membranes, for example, by sonic oscillation. The cell membrane fraction, prepared by gentle lysis, has been found in a variety of bacteria to contain the whole complement of cytochromes (Weibull, 1953; Marr, 1960).

The quantitative estimation of cytochromes in tissues and intact microorganisms by spectrophotometry is difficult, since the pigments are not readily extractable and examination in situ is liable to be inaccurate because of light scattering in turbid preparations. Measurement of the anaerobic-minus-aerobic difference spectra with double-beam spectrophotometers has largely overcome these problems (Chance, 1954; Smith, 1954). The values for cytochrome concentration shown in Table 2–4 have been computed from data derived by various methods including measurement of difference spectra and by direct extraction. Though the accuracy of the estimations is variable they serve to show that the cytochrome content is low when compared with that of the hemoglobins (Table 2–1) and chlorophylls (Table 2–5). Their quantitative contribution to the total tetrapyrroles in organisms that make either hemoglobin or chlorophyll is therefore slight. The cytochrome content shows quite wide variation between different organs and tissues from animals and is proportional to the oxidative activity (Drabkin, 1951). In microorganisms the degree of aerobiosis has a marked influence on cytochrome concentration (see Chapter 5).

Cytochromes Associated with Anaerobic Electron Transport. Cytochromes were originally thought to be associated only with aerobic electron transport mechanisms and this was supported by their absence in the strictly anaerobic bacteria of the genus *Clostridium*, which derive their energy by fermentation. One of the most interesting developments of the last decade has been the discovery of functional cytochromes in some groups of strictly anaerobic bacteria and in photosynthetic tissues (Newton and Kamen, 1961; Kamen, 1963).

Desulfovibrio desulfuricans, an obligate anaerobe which utilizes sulfate as terminal electron acceptor, is rich in a c-type cytochrome (cytochrome c_3); this hemoprotein accounts for about 0.3 per cent of the weight of the dried cells (Postgate, 1956, 1961). The purified cytochrome has two iron porphyrin (heme c) prosthetic groups per mole of protein and has the lowest potential (-0.205 volt) of the known cytochromes. There is evidence that it functions in electron transport in the reduction of sulfate to sulfide but its precise function in the electron transport chain is yet to be established (Postgate, 1959). Cytochromes probably participate in the analogous process of denitrification in which nitrate acts as terminal electron acceptor, being reduced to nitrogen. Denitrifying bacteria are rich in b- and c-type cytochromes, and the reduced forms of these pigments are oxidized by nitrate in cell extracts (Newton and Kamen, 1961).

The presence of a b-type cytochrome in *Bacteroides ruminicola*, an important species of ruminal bacteria, is of particular interest (White, Bryant, and Caldwell, 1962). These organisms ferment glucose by cytochrome-linked reactions; the importance of such reactions in the metabolism of these strict anaerobes is shown by the fact that many of them require hemin as a growth factor (Bryant and Robinson, 1962; see Chapter 3). In cell suspensions the reduced cytochrome is reoxidized by fumarate and it is likely that the cytochrome-linked reduction of fumarate to succinate plays a major part in the fermentative mechanisms of these rumen bacteria. Another strict anaerobe isolated from rumen, *Vibrio succinogenes*, is rich in both *b*- and *c*-type cytochromes (Jacobs and Wolin, 1963a, b; see Table 2–4). This organism obtains energy for growth by coupling oxidation of hydrogen or formate to the reduction of fumarate or nitrate via cytochrome-linked reactions.

The possibility that cytochromes are involved in electron transport associated with photosynthesis was suggested by the discovery of cytochrome f and cytochrome b_6 in leaf chloroplasts (Hill and Scarisbrick, 1951; Hartree, 1957; Kamen, 1963). The chloroplast hemoproteins differ from those found in the chlorophyll-less regions of the plants. Soon after, cytochromes were demonstrated in photosynthetic bacteria (Vernon and Kamen, 1954). All groups of photosynthetic bacteria, which include the strictly anaerobic green and red sulfur bacteria as well as the facultatively photoheterotrophic Athiorhodaceae, contain *c*-type cytochromes. These are present in high concentration; for example, about 0.5 per cent of the dry weight of the green sulfur organism, *Chlorobium thiosulfatophilum* consists of *c*-group cytochromes (Gibson, 1961). Several of these cytochromes have been purified and studied in detail (Kamen, 1963). Cytochromes of the *b* group have also been observed in the Athiorhodaceae. A unique type of hemoprotein in this group of organisms as well as in the red sulfur bacteria is RHP (*Rhodospirillum* hemeprotein or cytochromoid), present in about the same concentration as *c*-type cytochromes (Table 2–4). This hemoprotein has been purified from *Rhodospirillum rubrum* and *Chromatium* (Bartsch and Kamen, 1958; 1960). It contains two heme groups, both identical with heme *c*, and the reduced form exhibits a heterogeneous α band with maxima at 547 and 565 mμ.

The cytochromes of the photosynthetic bacteria are found in the chromatophores together with the chlorophyll and carotenoids (see page 32). Their function in electron-transfer reactions associated with chlorophyll activation by light is suggested by the light-dependent oxidation of the reduced cytochromes in whole cells or chromatophore preparations (Smith and Chance, 1958; Smith and Baltscheffsky, 1959; Nishimura and Chance, 1963). There seems to be little doubt that these cytochromes are intimately associated with photosynthetic phosphorylation in chromatophores but their sequence in the electron transport chain and the mechanism of coupling to the phosphorylating systems is yet to be determined.

2–3   CATALASE AND PEROXIDASE

Enzymes that react with hydrogen peroxide are widely distributed in animals, plants, and microbes and may be classified according to the reaction they catalyze.

Catalase decomposes hydrogen peroxide as follows:

$$2H_2O_2 \rightarrow 2H_2O + O_2$$

It also exhibits peroxidatic activity (vide infra) and catalyzes, for instance, the oxidation by hydrogen peroxide of ethanol to acetaldehyde (Keilin and Hartree, 1945; Herbert and Pinsent, 1948). Catalase has been isolated in crystalline form from the liver and red blood cells of various animals (Lemberg and Legge, 1949) and from *Micrococcus lysodeikticus* (Herbert and Pinsent, 1948). All contain four moles of hematin per mole of protein (molecular weight about 230,000). In animal tissues catalase is confined mainly to liver, kidney, and erythrocytes (Dixon and Webb, 1964). It is found in most microorganisms that have a cytochrome system, *Acetobacter peroxydans* being an exception. In *M. lysodeikticus* catalase comprises about 2 per cent of the dry weight (Herbert and Pinsent, 1948), whereas a mutant strain of *Rhodopseudomonas spheroides*, isolated from a medium containing 0.1 *M* hydrogen peroxide, produces up to 25 per cent of its dry weight as this hemoprotein (Clayton and Smith, 1960).

Peroxidases catalyze the oxidation by hydrogen peroxide of substrates such as aromatic amines as follows:

$$H_2A + H_2O_2 \rightarrow A + 2H_2O$$

A number of different peroxidases have been isolated from a variety of biological materials but the most well-studied are from plant sources. The horse-radish enzyme contains one mole of hematin per mole of protein (molecular weight 40,000). Many of the other peroxidases do not appear to be iron porphyrin enzymes (Lemberg and Legge, 1949; Dolin, 1961).

Although catalase has been of great value to biochemists studying the mechanism of enzyme action, its importance in vivo is less clear. It could function in the removal of toxic hydrogen peroxide produced by autooxidation of reduced flavins, but such autooxidation is unlikely to be a major problem in organisms with a cytochrome system, since direct reaction of flavoproteins with oxygen (at physiological pressures) occurs at a far slower rate than the reaction with cytochromes. The peroxidases (and catalase in its peroxidative capacity) could function in tissue oxidation by rendering hydrogen peroxide available as terminal hydrogen acceptor. A peroxidase hemoprotein has been purified from yeast which oxidizes reduced cytochrome c (Abrams, Altschul, and Hogness, 1942). Other cytochrome c peroxidases have also been found in microorganisms but their prosthetic group is not known (Lenhof and Kaplan, 1956). Under physiological conditions the origin of the hydrogen peroxide required for these reactions is obscure and until this is established their significance remains in doubt (Dolin, 1961).

2–4   TRYPTOPHAN PYRROLASE

Tryptophan pyrrolase, which catalyzes the oxidation of tryptophan to formylkynurenine, is a hemoprotein that does not fall into any of the categories discussed so far. The enzyme, purified from a tryptophan-grown *Pseudomonad*, has an iron porphyrin prosthetic group, the pyridine hemochrome of which differs from known hemochromes (Tanaka and Knox, 1959). The reaction mechanism involves direct oxygenation with molecular oxygen by the ferrous enzyme; the ferric enzyme is inactive but is reduced to the active form by hydrogen peroxide in the presence of tryptophan. Its ability to combine with oxygen in the ferrous state without oxidation of the iron therefore resembles the behavior of hemoglobin. The enzyme has also been purified from rat liver (Greengard and Feigelson, 1962; Tokuyama and Knox, 1964). Unlike the bacterial enzyme and other well-studied hemoproteins, liver tryptophan pyrrolase is readily dissociable and the apoenzyme is activated by hematin, after reduction in situ to heme. In other respects, such as inhibition by carbon monoxide and activation by hydrogen peroxide plus tryptophan, the bacterial and liver enzymes seem to be similar (Tanaka and Knox, 1959).

2–5   CHLOROPHYLLS

The chlorophylls comprise by far the major tetrapyrrole pigment in photosynthetic organisms as would be expected from their function in trapping radiant energy, which is the basis of the photosynthetic way of life. They therefore occupy a role analogous to that of hemoglobin in higher animals, which depend on oxygen as terminal oxidant.

Plant Chlorophylls. Chlorophyll *a* is the most ubiquitous of the plant pigments of this class and occurs in all plants and algae that rely on radiant energy. It is accompanied by chlorophyll *b* in the higher plants and most green algae, whereas the brown and red algae have chlorophyll *c* and *d*, respectively, in place of chlorophyll *b*. The blue-green algae contain only chlorophyll *a* (Rabinowitch, 1945; Smith and Benitez, 1955; French, 1960; Bogorad, 1962).

The concentration of the chlorophylls in plants and algaes varies considerably with the species, age, and environment. With adequate nutrition best yields are obtained at moderate temperatures and with low to medium light intensities. Under such conditions the total chlorophyll content of most leaves is about 1 per cent of the dry weight, whereas unicellular algae contain up to about 5 per cent of their dry weight as chlorophyll (Rabinowitch, 1945). The chlorophyll *a* content is usually two to three times that of the *b* component but this ratio is subject to environmental influence. The total chlorophyll concentration is fifty to one hundred times greater than that of the total hemes (Table 2–5).

The chlorophylls are located in the chloroplasts of higher plants and algae with the exception of the blue-green algae, which lack a defined chloroplast. Electron microscopy has shown that the chloroplasts of most plants contain subunits or grana which have a lamellar structure and the pigments are thought to be part of this structure (Granick, 1961a). Chloroplasts, in which grana are not discernible, nevertheless exhibit lamellar structures that seem to be typical of all chlorophyllous plant tissues including the blue-green algae (Chapman and Salton, 1962).

The chlorophylls are bound within these structures to lipoprotein complexes, which may be extracted with detergents such as digitonin (Kupke and French, 1960; Wolken, 1961). The relation of the extracted preparations to the functional macromolecular complexes in the intact cells is yet to be established.

Chlorophylls of Photosynthetic Bacteria. It was believed that red sulfur bacteria (Thiorhodaceae) and the red and brown nonsulfur bacteria (Athiorhodaceae) all contain the form of chlorophyll designated bacteriochlorophyll by Hans Fischer. This assumption must now be reexamined carefully since another pigment (bacteriochlorophyll *b*) has been identified in a species of *Rhodopseu-*

domonad; its structure remains to be determined (Eimhjellen, Aasmundrud, and Jensen, 1963).

The chlorophylls of the green sulfur bacteria are quite distinct from bacteriochlorophyll and have the dihydroporphyrin ring structure of chlorophyll *a*, although their structure is yet to be fully established (Lascelles, 1963). All organisms of this family which have been examined have *Chlorobium* chlorophyll 660 with the one exception of a strain of *Chlorobium thiosulfatophilum,* which has a distinctly different pigment (650; Stanier and Smith, 1960). The significance of the exceptional chlorophyll in the one apparently unique strain of *Chlorobium* might fall into place when the structures have been determined and the biosynthetic pathway elucidated.

The amount of chlorophyll in photosynthetic bacteria is similar to that in unicellular algae and is about one hundred times greater than the concentration of total hemes (Table 2–5). Just as in plants, the chlorophyll level in bacteria is greatly influenced by the environment; this is discussed more fully in Chapter 5.

The chlorophyll of the photosynthetic bacteria is combined to macromolecular units, the chromatophores, which are separable from cell extracts by differential centrifugation (Schachman, Pardee, and Stanier, 1952; Bergeron, 1959; Lascelles, 1962a). The chromatophores contain the entire complement of photosynthetic pigments as well as cytochromes and other components of the electron transport chain and they are rich in protein and phospholipid. The appearance of the isolated particles in the electron microscope agrees with their appearance in sections of intact organisms. The lamellar structure, so characteristic of the chloroplasts of plant cells, has been definitively established in only two photosynthetic bacteria, *Rhodospirillum molischianum* (Giesbrecht and Drews, 1962) and *Rhodomicrobium vannielii,* which lacks discernible chromatophores (Vatter, Douglas, and Wolfe, 1959). The inability to detect a lamellar structure in other bacteria does not preclude the possibility that the chromatophores have a fine structure that is beyond the resolution of the techniques used so far.

2–6   PORPHYRINS

Free porphyrins have no known biological function and they accumulate as by-products of the normal biosynthetic pathway leading to the functional tetrapyrroles, namely, the hemes and chlorophylls. Under normal circumstances only small amounts of porphyrins occur in nature. This demonstrates clearly the efficiency of the control mechanisms operating in tetrapyrrole biosynthesis, which allow very little waste of intermediates.

Porphyrins in Animals. The erythrocytes of normal animals contain small amounts of proto- and coproporphyrin (about 13 and 0.3 μg, respectively, per 100 ml of red cells in the human); the quantities of these porphyrins may increase by tenfold or more in pernicious anemia and lead-induced anemia (Schwarz and Wikoff, 1952). Coproporphyrin (mainly type 1) and smaller amounts of uroporphyrin occur in normal urine; they are excreted primarily as the colorless porphyrinogens that are spontaneously oxidized to the parent porphyrin (Falk, 1954). The excretion of copro- and uroporphyrins (free porphyrin and precursor) by normal males amounts to about 100 and 20 μg, respectively, per day.

The porphyria diseases are characterized by the excretion of large quantities of porphyrins or precursors in the urine. Three main forms of these diseases have been recognized (Falk, 1954; Wintrobe, 1961; Granick and Mauzerall, 1961; Granick, 1962; Goldberg and Rimington, 1962). Congenital or erythropoietic porphyria results in the deposition of porphyrins in the skin, bones, and other tissues, causing photosensitivity. The urine is rich in uroporphyrin I. In acute porphyria there is no accumulation in the tissues but during an attack porphobilinogen and δ-aminolevulinate (intermediates in tetrapyrrole synthesis) are excreted (Granick and Vanden Schrieck, 1955). The porphobilinogen is converted spontaneously to uroporphyrin, the excretion of which may amount to about 50 mg per day. Porphyria cutanea tarda is characterized by high concentrations of uro- and coproporphyrins in both urine and feces. Although these diseases have been studied mainly in humans they occur in other animals such as beef cattle. One bullock, afflicted with congenital porphyria, has been exploited as a rich source of uro- and coproporphyrins (Jørgensen and With, 1955; 1963).

Acute porphyria can be induced artificially by certain drugs, the most important being Sedormid (allyl-isopropyl-acetyl urea) and allyl-isopropylacetamide (Goldberg and Rimington, 1962). The use of these drugs with experimental animals may help to understand the disease in humans.

Porphyrin Accumulation by Microorganisms. In his survey of natural products for the occurrence of porphyrins Hans Fischer noted that some yeasts and tubercle bacteria were rich sources. Since that time porphyrins have been found in the cells or, more commonly, in the culture fluids of many other microorganisms.

Accumulation by nonphotosynthetic organisms. The first notable contribution to an understanding of porphyrin accumulation in microorganisms was made by Pappenheimer (1947) who showed that *Corynebacterium diphtheriae* accumulated these pigments, together with toxin, only in media containing low concentrations of iron. The yield of porphyrin and toxin decreased as the amount of iron was increased beyond a certain critical level.

Since then a similar relation between iron and porphyrin formation has been noted with many bacteria as well as with yeasts and the ciliate *Tetrahymena* (Table 2–6). Besides iron, other environ-

Table 2–6   Porphyrin accumulation by nonphotosynthetic microorganisms[a]

Organisms	Special growth conditions	Amount, mg/liter	Predominant porphyrins
Coryne. diphtheriae	Low iron	7	Copro. III
Coryne. erythrogenes	Low iron	49	Copro. III; uro. I
Arthrobact. globiformis	Low iron	33	Copro. III
Propionibact. shermannii	Low iron	9	Copro. III
Micro. lysodeikticus	Low iron	6	Copro. III
B. subtilis	Low iron	5	Copro. III
Sacch. anamensis	Low iron	298[*]	Copro. I
Tetrahymena vorax	Low iron	6	Uro. and copro. III; proto.
Streptomyces griseus	Low iron	—	Copro. III[c]
B. cereus	Anaerobic	0.14	Copro. III
Sacch. cerevisiae	Anaerobic	0.09	Copro.
Staph. aureus	Anaerobic	—	—
Mycobacterium spp.	—	8–18[*]	Copro. III

[a] From Lascelles (1962b) where full literature references are given. The amounts are for porphyrin in the culture fluids except for those marked[*], where the porphyrin is accumulated in the cells (mg/kg wet weight). When coproporphyrin III is predominant it accounts for at least 95 per cent of the total but is usually accompanied by smaller amounts of uroporphyrin and traces of others. To facilitate comparison with the values in Table 2–7, 1 mg coproporphyrin = 1.5 μmole.

[b] — Denotes that information is not available.

[c] The porphyrin is in the mycelia (Musilek, 1962).

mental conditions influenced porphyrin accumulation. In particular, anaerobic conditions favor their formation by some organisms.

The amount of porphyrin in cultures varies considerably, but the frequent occurrence of coproporphyrin III as the predominant pigment (Table 2–6) is striking.

The significance of these accumulations is not yet fully understood. The correlation with iron deficiency suggests that they are formed when the ability to form hemoproteins is limited. This is supported by the observation that the levels of cytochrome b_1 and catalase are lower in iron-deficient cultures of C. diphtheriae, which accumulate porphyrins, than in iron-rich cultures (Pappenheimer and Hendee, 1947). The effect of iron is discussed in more detail in Chapters 3 and 5.

Accumulation by photosynthetic bacteria. Van Niel (1944) observed that the culture fluids of many photosynthetic bacteria of the Athiorhodaceae group contained a red pigment, later identified as a mixture of porphyrins containing coproporphyrin III (at least 95 per cent) and uroporphyrin III (2 to 3 per cent) (Lascelles, 1956a). These organisms appear to be the richest source of porphyrins in the microbial world and the accumulation of the pigments is connected with the synthesis of bacteriochlorophyll. As with nonphotosynthetic bacteria, coproporphyrin formation is influenced by iron, being maximal under iron-deficient conditions. On the other hand, the concentration of bacteriochlorophyll in the cells is maximal only with adequate iron, so that there is an inverse relation between the accumulation of coproporphyrin and the formation of bacteriochlorophyll, governed by the amount of iron (Table 2–7).

Table 2–7   Effect of iron on porphyrin and bacteriochlorophyll formation by photosynthetic bacteria[a]

Organism	Coproporphyrin III		Bacteriochlorophyll	
	−	+	−	+
R. spheroides	82	3	13	36
R. capsulata	19	6	11	23
R. palustris	12	2	8	24
R. gelatinosa	105	66	10	29

[a] From Lascelles (1962b). The amounts are in μm-moles per ml of culture, the porphyrin being in the culture fluids and the bacteriochlorophyll in the cells. Iron was omitted (−) or added (+) at 10 μm-moles per ml.

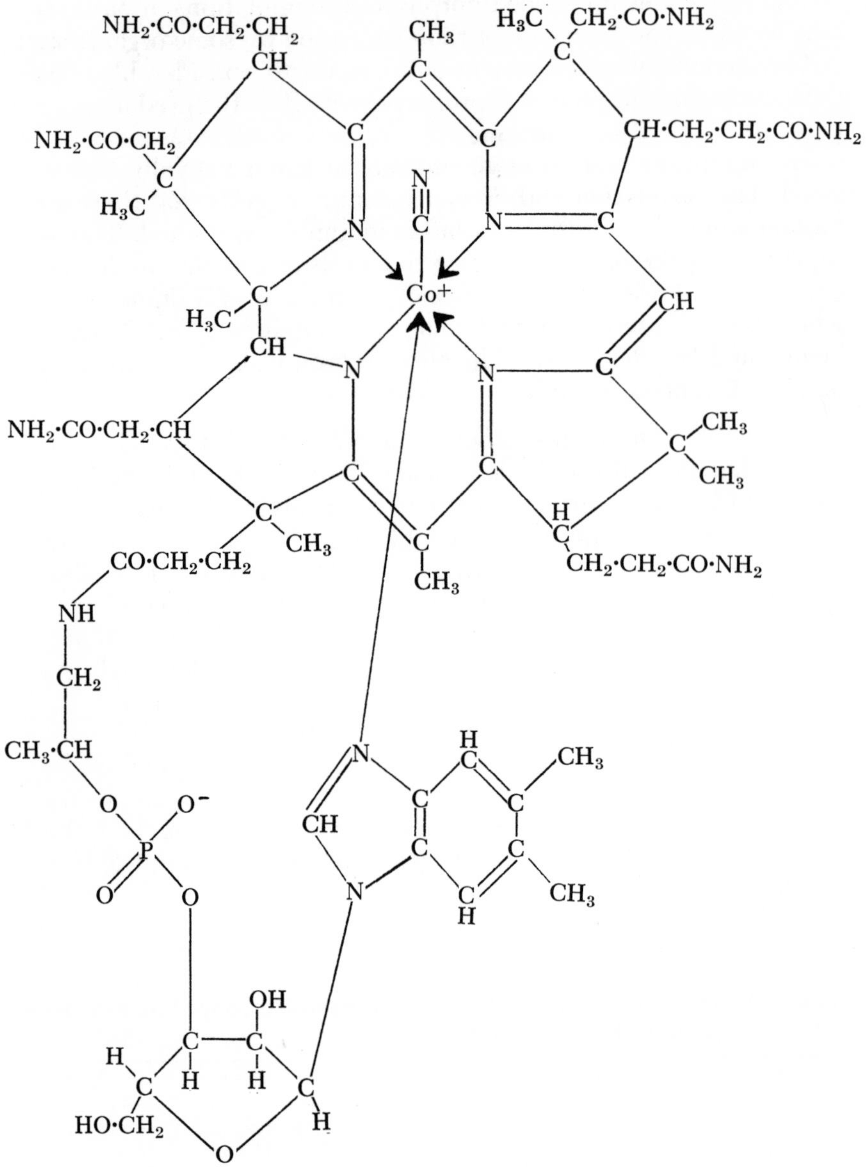

Figure 2–2   Cyanocobalamin.

Many of the Athiorhodaceae grow aerobically in the dark but under these circumstances both bacteriochlorophyll synthesis and porphyrin accumulation is repressed, again pointing to the association of the porphyrins with bacteriochlorophyll formation.

Besides copro- and uroporphyrins, magnesium protoporphyrin monomethyl ester and dihydroporphyrins have been found in cultures of Athiorhodaceae. These substances are intermediates or by-products of the synthesis of bacteriochlorophyll and their significance is considered in Chapter 4.

2–7   VITAMIN B₁₂

The vitamin B_{12} group (also known as cobalamins, corphyrins or cobamides) comprises a large number of compounds that all have a porphyrin-like nucleus (corrin) with a coordinate cobalt atom. Of these, cyanocobalamin was the first to be identified chemically (Figure 2–2). The structure of the corrin nucleus is sufficiently similar to that of the porphyrins to warrant mention under the general heading of tetrapyrroles; the absence of a methene bridge C atom between rings C and D should be noted; the various derivatives of cyanocobalamin vary in the following respects: (1) the cyanide group is replaced by other anions or by an adenosyl residue, the adenosyl derivatives being the coenzyme forms of the vitamin (Barker, 1961); (2) the nucleotide moiety is absent or substituted; (3) the corrin carboxamide groups may be substituted, generally by propionamide groups. Information about the chemistry and biological activity of the cobalamins is given in recent reviews (E. L. Smith, 1960; Brown and Reynolds, 1963; Heinrich, 1963).

The pyrrole rings of the corrin component moiety probably arise from the same precursors as those of the tetrapyrroles (Bray and Shemin, 1963). It is therefore of some significance that rich sources include species of Streptomyces and Propionibacteria, which also accumulate porphyrins. However, cobalamins are also present in strict anaerobes of the genus Clostridium, which do not form tetrapyrroles; their concentration is comparable to that of cytochromes in aerobic bacteria (up to 0.11 μm-mole per mg dry weight; Stadtman, 1960). The biosynthesis of the cobalamins in anaerobes certainly deserves investigation.

3

THE BIOSYNTHESIS

OF TETRAPYRROLES: PATHWAY

TO HEMES AND HEMOPROTEINS

The ubiquity of tetrapyrroles in living matter, and the fact that preformed tetrapyrroles are required as growth factors by only a very few organisms, shows that the ability to form these compounds from simple precursors is common. As far as we know the same biosynthetic pathway is used by all forms of life; even the formation of chlorophyll proceeds by a pathway common to that leading to hemes up to the stage of protoporphyrin. In considering the biosynthesis of these pigments, the iron branch (Granick, 1950a), which leads ultimately to the hemoproteins, is discussed in this chapter, and the magnesium branch culminating in the chlorophylls, in the next.

3–1 PATHWAY TO PROTOPORPHYRIN

The work that has led to the establishment of the pathway to protoporphyrin (Scheme 3–1) can be divided into three stages. In the first, isotopically labeled compounds were used with intact animals or, later, with whole blood, and the incorporation of isotope was followed into the heme of hemoglobin. The source of

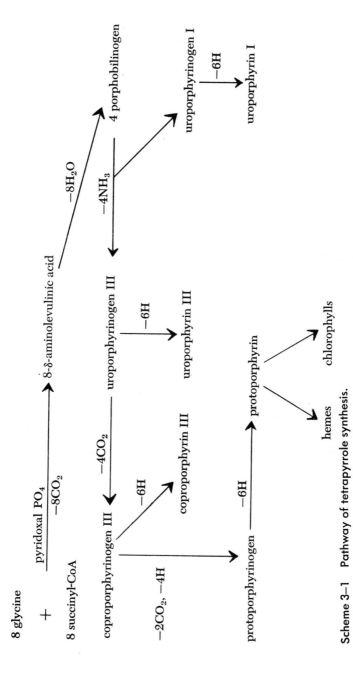

Scheme 3–1   Pathway of tetrapyrrole synthesis.

39

each atom of the protoporphyrin molecule was elucidated by the brilliant exploitation of these techniques, particularly by Shemin and colleagues (Shemin, 1955a, b). The recognition of δ-amino-levulinate and porphobilinogen as intermediates marked the second stage. In the final stage individual enzymic steps have been studied with preparations from animals, plants, and micro-organisms.

Experiments with Isotopes. The first indication that protoporphyrin was built up from small molecules was provided by the demonstration of the incorporation into heme of deuterioacetate and N^{15}-glycine administered to rats and humans (Bloch and Rittenberg, 1945; Shemin and Rittenberg, 1946). Further progress depended on the development of methods for the degradation of the labeled protoporphyrin so that the origin of each atom could be traced (Wittenberg and Shemin, 1949, 1950; Muir and Neuberger, 1950; Shemin and Wittenberg, 1951). These studies showed that glycine

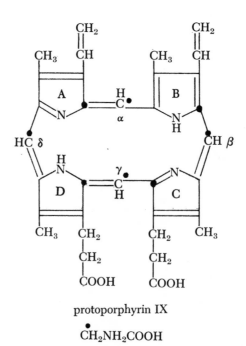

protoporphyrin IX

$\overset{\bullet}{C}H_2NH_2COOH$

Figure 3–1   Incorporation of α-C atom of glycine into protoporphyrin (reproduced from Shemin, 1955a).

provides not only all four N atoms but also the methene bridge C atoms and one C atom in each pyrrole ring, in the α position under the vinyl and propionic acid sidechains (Figure 3–1). Only the α-C atom of glycine contributes to the protoporphyrin and over-all, eight molecules of glycine are used for the synthesis of one of protoporphyrin. Similar studies with C^{14}-acetate showed that the rest of the carbon atoms are derived from this molecule. The relative distribution in the protoporphyrin molecule of the methyl and carboxyl C atoms of acetate suggested that it is incorporated as an unsymmetrical four carbon compound arising from the tricarboxylic acid cycle. This was confirmed by the demonstration that succinate is the precursor of 26 of the 34 C atoms of protoporphyrin and the pattern of C^{14} distribution shows that it is utilized as a unit (Figure 3–2). Malonate inhibited the incorporation of succinate labeled in the methylene carbon atoms but not succinate labeled in the carboxyls. This indicated that the intermediate that condenses with glycine is an active form of succinate, presumed to be succinyl CoA; this can arise directly from succinate or via the tricarboxylic acid cycle from α-ketoglutarate (Shemin and Kumin, 1952; see Scheme 3–2).

Tissue preparations used in isotopic studies. Much of this early work was performed with intact avian erythrocytes, which are nucleated and which can synthesize hemoglobin. In mammals the ability to form hemoglobin is found only at a certain stage in the development of the erythrocyte in the bone marrow; the mature red cell, which lacks both DNA and RNA, has lost this capacity (London, 1961). However, immature mammalian erythrocytes (reticulocytes), containing RNA although not DNA, do form hemo-

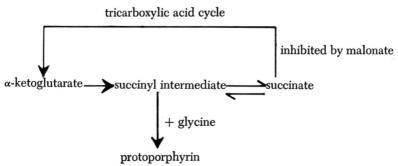

Scheme 3–2   Origin of the succinyl intermediate.

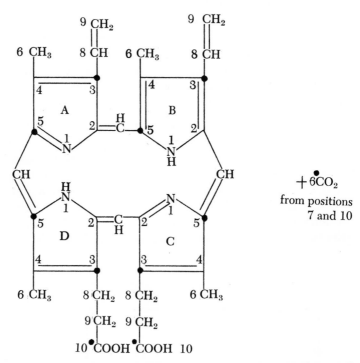

Figure 3–2   Incorporation of 1,4-labeled succinate into protoporphyrin (after Shemin, 1955a).

globin. Normal mammalian blood contains few reticulocytes and does not synthesize heme as measured by incorporation of labeled glycine; in contrast the blood of subjects with sickle cell anemia, which has a high reticulocyte count, is able to form heme (London, Shemin, and Rittenberg, 1949). Reticulocyte production is enhanced by bleeding or by the administration of phenyl hydrazine (London, Shemin, and Rittenberg, 1950), and blood from mammals treated in this way has also been used as experimental material. Bone marrow preparations have not found much favor due to the technical difficulties involved in obtaining active material.

The next technique developed was the use of hemolyzed red cell preparations, thereby overcoming permeability barriers (Shemin and Kumin, 1952; Wriston, Lack, and Shemin, 1955; Dresel and Falk, 1954).

δ-Aminolevulinate and Porphobilinogen as Intermediates. The recognition of δ-aminolevulinate (ALA) and porphobilinogen (PBG) (Figure 3–3) as intermediates between glycine and protoporphyrin were major breakthroughs in the field. ALA was deduced to be a product of the condensation of glycine and the succinyl derivative by armchair chemistry. These speculations were justified by the demonstration that ALA labeled with N^{15} and with C^{14} in the δ-C atom is actively incorporated into protoporphyrin and gives the same labeling pattern as that given by glycine (Shemin and Russell, 1953). In confirmation, ALA was shown to be converted by hemolyzates to porphyrins (Neuberger and Scott, 1953; Shemin, Russell, and Abramsky, 1955).

There is isotopic evidence that ALA is not converted solely to tetrapyrroles in animal tissues but that it is metabolized by a route that results in the conversion of the δ-C (arising from the α-C atom of glycine) to a one-C fragment. To account for these observations Shemin (1955a, b) proposed that glycine is metabolized by a succinate-glycine cycle in which ALA figures as a key intermediate. The operation of this cycle has not yet been fully validated.

The initial demonstration of PBG as an intermediate was shown by a somewhat different approach. This substance had been recognized for many years in the urine of subjects with acute porphyria. Relatively recently it was isolated from such urines and its structure was identified (Westall, 1952; Cookson and Rimington, 1954). Falk, Dresel, and Rimington (1953) showed that it is converted with high efficiency to a mixture of porphyrins by chick

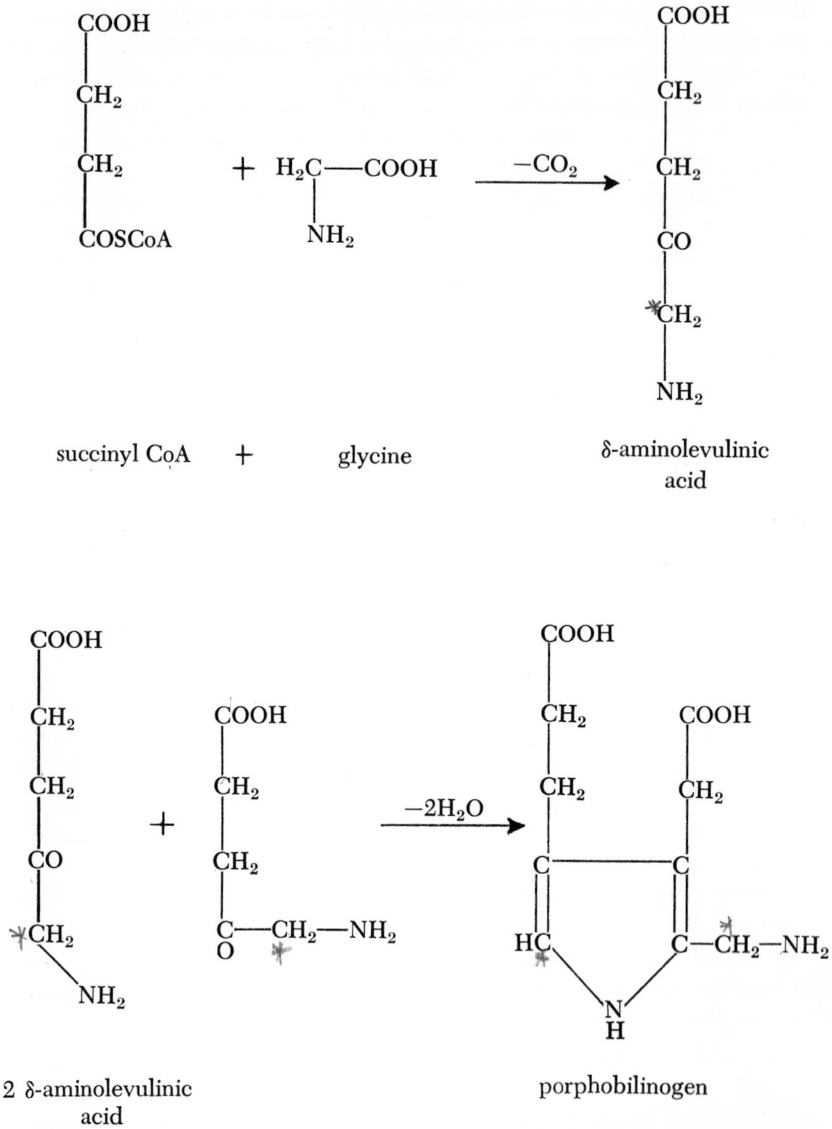

succinyl CoA   +   glycine   δ-aminolevulinic
                                acid

2 δ-aminolevulinic   porphobilinogen
   acid

Figure 3–3   The reactions catalyzed by ALA synthetase and ALA dehydratase.

hemolyzates. In these preparations PBG is converted at the same rate and to the same end products as ALA and its behavior therefore indicates it is an intermediate between ALA and tetrapyrroles (Dresel and Falk, 1956).

Enzymic Steps. The establishment of ALA and PBG as intermediates in protoporphyrin synthesis was a great stimulus to the field and resulted in a broader experimental approach. Avian red cell preparations were followed by preparations from other animal tissues, from plants and, most recently, from bacteria. The activity of such preparations is sufficient to enable net synthesis of products to be measured without resorting to isotopic techniques. Biochemists aim ultimately to demonstrate an entire reaction sequence with purified enzymes, but this has yet to be fully realized. However, enzymes catalyzing some of the steps have been isolated in purified form.

Formation of ALA. Net synthesis of ALA from glycine and succinate or α-ketoglutarate was originally demonstrated with particles from lysed erythrocytes of anemic chickens; the reaction was stimulated by CoA and pyridoxal phosphate (Laver, Neuberger, and Udenfriend, 1958). After freeze-drying, the particles utilized succinyl CoA for the synthesis (Gibson, Laver, and Neuberger, 1958). Soon after this work, ALA synthesis from glycine and succinyl CoA was shown with cell-free extracts from the photosynthetic bacterium *R. spheroides* (Kikuchi, Kumar, Talmage, and Shemin, 1958; Gibson, 1958).

The bacterial extracts are considerably more active than the red cell preparations and have consequently been used in detailed studies of the enzyme, known as ALA synthetase (Figure 3–3). The extracts catalyzed ALA formation from glycine and succinyl CoA, either added as such or generated from succinate, ATP, and CoA by succinic thiokinase (Kikuchi et al., 1958). Pyridoxal phosphate is an essential cofactor for the synthetase.

The participation of CoA (as succinyl CoA) and pyridoxal phosphate in the ALA synthetase reaction accounts for the observations, first made over twenty years ago, that nutritional deficiencies of pyridoxine and pantothenate cause hypochromic anemia (Chick, Macrae, Martin, and Martin, 1938; Carter, Macfarlane, O'Brien, and Robb-Smith, 1945; Jukes, 1953). More recent work, prior to the studies with the isolated enzyme, showed that the site of action of the vitamins is at the initial condensation stage. Vitamin-deficient protozoa (*Tetrahymena vorax*) do not form porphyrins from glycine although they are active with ALA as substrate (Lascelles, 1957); similar findings were made with hemolysates from vitamin-deficient ducks (Schulman and Richert, 1957).

There is evidence that iron may participate in the action of ALA synthetase in some tissues. The enzyme in preparations from avian red cells is stimulated by iron (Brown, 1958; Vogel, Richert, Pixley, and Schulman, 1960); in iron-deficient leaf discs incorporation of C^{14}-α-ketoglutarate into chlorophyll is considerably reduced when compared with normal tissue, whereas the incorporation of labeled ALA is not impaired (Marsh, Evans, and Matrone, 1963a, b). There is no evidence that iron is involved in the action of the enzyme from bacteria, and the fact that iron deficiency actually enhances porphyrin accumulation argues against this (see Chapter 5).

The ALA synthetase enzyme seems to be labile but is protected to some extent by mercaptoethanol and chelators; a reproducible procedure that gives a tenfold purification includes these stabilizing agents (Burnham and Lascelles, 1963). The mechanism of action of the synthetase is not known. The kinetics of evolution of labeled carbon dioxide from carboxyl-labeled glycine accord with a concerted condensation-decarboxylation reaction rather than with a mechanism that involves the intermediate formation of free α-amino-β-ketoadipic acid (Kikuchi, Kumar, and Shemin, 1959). The fact that red cell preparations and bacterial extracts with ALA synthetase activity also catalyze the condensation of glycine with acetyl CoA to give aminoacetone (and analogous reactions) suggests that the enzyme is not specific for succinyl CoA. In liver mitochondria, however, there is evidence that the reactions are catalyzed by different enzymes (Urata and Granick, 1963).

There is little information about the distribution of ALA synthetase. It is present in photosynthetic bacteria related to *R. spheroides*, but has not been detected in extracts of many other bacteria (Burnham and Lascelles, unpublished). The organisms that have been assayed synthesize tetrapyrroles in the form of porphyrins and hemoproteins and presumably contain the enzyme; why it has not been detected in cell-free extracts is unknown. In animal tissues, apart from the immature red cells, it has been detected in guinea pig liver mitochondria. In normal mitochondria the enzyme level is low, but is increased fortyfold by administration of 3,5-dicarbethoxy-1,4-dihydrocollidine (Granick and Urata, 1963).

Conversion of ALA to PBG. The enzyme responsible for this reaction, ALA dehydratase (Figure 3–3), is widely distributed in nature and has been found in preparations from animals, plants, and bacteria (Gibson, Neuberger, and Scott, 1955). Liver is a rich source although other tissues, particularly kidney and bone marrow, are also active; the level of the enzyme in liver and kidney is doubled in animals with sedormid-induced porphyria. Unlike ALA synthetase, the dehydratase is confined to the soluble fraction of liver and of hemolysates.

ALA dehydratase has been purified from ox liver (Gibson et al., 1955), from erythrocytes (Granick and Mauzerall, 1958) and from *R. spheroides* (Burnham and Lascelles, 1963). In all cases, the enzyme appears to require thiol groups for activity and the bacterial enzyme, at least, is activated by potassium ions.

PBG to Uroporphyrinogen. PBG is converted to a mixture of porphyrins, predominantly uro- and coproporphyrins by hemolysates and by crude enzyme preparations from algae and bacteria. The copro- and uroporphyrins arise by oxidation, which may be partly or wholly spontaneous, of the corresponding porphyrinogens (Figure 3–4); the autooxidation is photocatalyzed and is sensitized by the porphyrin product (Mauzerall and Granick, 1958). The fact that labeled uroporphyrinogen III, but not the corresponding porphyrin, is incorporated by hemolysates into heme was the first indication that the porphyrinogens are the true intermediates (Neve, Labbe, and Aldrich, 1956).

Crude enzyme preparations are usually capable of forming the type III isomer but preparations from all sources can be readily modified to produce only uroporphyrinogen I by heating for short times at about 50°.

The work of Bogorad (1958a, b, c; 1963) has shown that the conversion of PBG to uroporphyrinogen III proceeds in at least two steps catalyzed by PBG deaminase and uroporphyrinogen III cosynthetase (originally known as uroporphyrin isomerase). The deaminase, free of the cosynthetase, has been isolated from spinach leaf where it is partly located in the chloroplasts (Bogorad, 1958a) and also from *R. spheroides* (Hoare and Heath, 1959). It catalyzes the over-all reaction

$$4PBG \rightarrow \text{uroporphyrinogen I} + 4NH_3$$

The type III isomer is not formed by the deaminase.

Crude deaminase preparations catalyze the oxidation of the

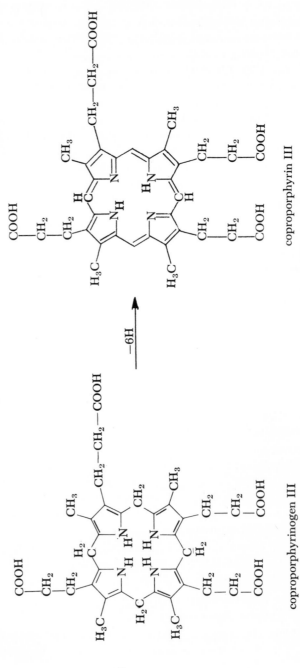

coproporphyrinogen III

coproporphyrin III

Figure 3-4   The oxidation of coproporphyrinogen III to coproporphyrin III.

48

colorless porphyrinogen to uroporphyrin I with intermediate formation of a compound with the spectral characteristics to be expected of a tetrapyrrole at an oxidation level between the porphyrinogen and the porphyrin. The same transformation is induced nonenzymically with iodine. The oxidase is more readily destroyed by heat than the deaminase, providing a method for obtaining deaminase preparations free of oxidase.

For the formation of the type III isomer, uroporphyrinogen cosynthetase is needed in addition to the deaminase. This enzyme has been prepared from wheat germ (Bogorad, 1958b). Uroporphyrinogen III is formed from PBG only when both enzymes are present simultaneously; the cosynthetase does not act on preformed uroporphyrinogen I. The over-all reaction may be formulated as follows:

$$4\text{PBG} \xrightarrow[\substack{\text{uroporphyrinogen III} \\ \text{cosynthetase}}]{\text{PBG deaminase}} \text{uroporphyrinogen III} + 4\text{NH}_3$$

Enzyme fractions have been prepared from erythrocytes that convert PBG to uroporphyrinogen III. These have not been resolved into component protein fractions, although heat treatment results in the formation of only the type I isomer (Granick and Mauzerall, 1958; Lockwood and Benson, 1960).

Despite wide speculation on the mechanism of conversion of PBG to uroporphyrinogen III, "the only hypotheses which are still not wholly excluded are those which have not yet been tested experimentally" (Bogorad and Marks, 1960). The data are compatible with a reaction catalyzed by the cosynthetase between PBG and a di- or tripyrrole, formed by the deaminase (Bogorad, 1963).

Uroporphyrinogen to Coproporphyrinogen. Partially purified preparations have been made from rabbit reticulocytes and from *R. spheroides*, which catalyze the decarboxylation of uroporphyrinogen to coproporphyrinogen (Mauzerall and Granick, 1958; Hoare and Heath, 1959). In both cases uroporphyrinogen (I or III) is the substrate and coproporphyrinogen the product; uroporphyrin is not converted. Porphyrins with 7, 6, and 5 carboxyl groups are detectable by chromatography during the conversion, showing that the decarboxylation proceeds in stages. Whether more than one enzyme is involved in the over-all reaction is not known.

Coproporphyrinogen to Protoporphyrin. The formation of protoporphyrin from ALA or PBG was first shown with crude preparations from red cells and hemolysates. Some preparations, although capable of forming uro- and coproporphyrins, synthesized little or no protoporphyrin unless supplemented with liver mitochondria. This suggested that the enzyme system responsible for protoporphyrin formation from coproporphyrinogen III is located in the mitochondria. This has now been confirmed by the isolation of a fraction (coproporphyrinogen oxidase) from ox liver mitochondria, which catalyzes the conversion of coproporphyrinogen III to protoporphyrin (Sano and Granick, 1961). The same reaction, termed coprogenase, has also been studied with crude preparations of ox liver mitochondria (Porra and Falk, 1963). The enzyme system is present in many other tissues besides liver; in that organ, at least, over 80 per cent of the activity is in the mitochondria (Sano and Granick, 1961).

The reaction in the mitochondrial preparations requires oxygen as the hydrogen acceptor. No other oxidant, including flavins, cytochrome c, and artificial electron acceptors, has yet been found to replace oxygen. During the conversion, an intermediate tricarboxylic tetrapyrrole with one vinyl and three propionic sidechains appears and then disappears. The immediate precursor of protoporphyrin is protoporphyrinogen. This has been demonstrated during the transformation of coproporphyrinogen III (Porra and Falk, 1963) and when added to mitochondrial preparations it is converted to the porphyrin (Sano and Granick, 1961). The reaction therefore may proceed in at least three stages.

$$
\begin{array}{c}
\text{coproporphyrinogen III} \\
\downarrow \begin{smallmatrix} -CO_2 \\ -2H \end{smallmatrix} \\
\text{tricarboxylic porphyrinogen} \\
\downarrow \begin{smallmatrix} -CO_2 \\ -2H \end{smallmatrix} \\
\text{protoporphyrinogen} \\
\downarrow -6H \\
\text{protoporphyrin}
\end{array}
$$

It is not known whether the complete transformation is catalyzed by a single enzyme or whether separate enzymes are involved in the oxidative decarboxylation of each propionic acid sidechain, and in the oxidation of protoporphyrinogen to protoporphyrin. Nor is anything known of the mechanism of the oxidative decarboxylation. Some of the intermediates may be protein-bound, since porphyrins combined to protein by covalent bounds have been detected during the conversion of coproporphyrinogen III to protoporphyrin by mitochondrial preparations (Porra and Falk, 1963).

Observations with microorganisms suggest that iron participates catalytically in the over-all reaction. Thus, coproporphyrin III, and not protoporphyrin, is accumulated predominantly by microorganisms under conditions of iron deficiency (see Table 2–6). Also, suspensions of iron-deficient *R. spheroides* and *Tetrahymena vorax* convert ALA to coproporphyrin III (with some uroporphyrin III) but protoporphyrin is formed only upon addition of iron (Lascelles, 1956a, b; 1957). It is therefore significant that the mitochondrial coproporphyrinogen III oxidase is inhibited by *o*-phenanthroline, a chelating agent with a high affinity for iron (Sano and Granick, 1961).

Recent work with leaf tissues does not support a role for iron in the conversion of coproporphyrinogen to protoporphyrin in higher plants, since ALA is converted to protoporphyrin and to chlorophyll by iron-deficient leaf discs (cow pea) at the same rate as normal preparations (Marsh, Evans, and Matrone, 1963a, b).

The involvement of CoA in the reaction is suggested by the fact that pantothenate-deficient cells of *T. vorax*, in the presence of adequate iron, form only uro- and coproporphyrin III from ALA, whereas normal cells form protoporphyrin (Lascelles, 1957).

The experiments with deficient organisms provide only indirect evidence for the participation of these factors. A study of the coproporphyrinogen III oxidase with purified cell-free preparations is needed to establish their roles.

3–2   INSERTION OF IRON INTO PROTOPORPHYRIN

The fact that iron complexes of uro- and coproporphyrin are not found in nature suggests strongly that the metal is incorporated at the stage of protoporphyrin in the biosynthesis of heme. Further support for this is given by the microorganisms that respond either to protoporphyrin or hemin as a growth factor.

Ferrous iron coordinates spontaneously with protoporphyrin under physiological conditions (Granick and Mauzerall, 1958); this raises the question of whether the final stage in heme formation is catalyzed by a specific enzyme. Evidence that the reaction is enzyme-catalyzed is provided by the microorganisms that require hemin as a growth factor and do not respond to protoporphyrin plus iron (see Section 3–3). Direct evidence for a specific enzyme has come from studies with purified preparations from rat liver mitochondria and from avian erythrocytes (Labbe and Hubbard,

1960; Schwarz, Goudsmit, Hill, Cartwright, and Wintrobe, 1961; Yoneyama, Ohyama, Sugita, and Yoshikawa, 1962). The enzyme system, known as ferrochelatase or heme synthetase, catalyzes the reaction

$$\text{protoporphyrin} + Fe^{2+} \rightarrow \text{heme} + 2H^+$$

It has also been found in extracts of microorganisms (Porra and Jones, 1963).

The rat liver enzyme is located in the mitochondria (Nishida and Labbe, 1959), and the purified preparation requires only a reducing agent such as glutathione as cofactor. Cobalt is as active as iron with this enzyme (Labbe and Hubbard, 1961), but with the erythrocyte preparation it is much less effective (Yoneyama et al., 1962). The enzyme from both sources appears to utilize only dicarboxylic porphyrins, and protoporphyrinogen is not used (Labbe, Hubbard, and Caughey, 1963). Porphyrin a, derived from the prosthetic group of cytochrome a, is not a substrate for the mitochondrial enzyme (Porra and Jones, 1963).

There is evidence for protein-bound intermediates in heme synthesis. With hemolysates, protein-bound protoporphyrin (formed by the hemolysates from labeled ALA) is more readily incorporated into heme than the free porphyrin (Sugita, 1962). Also, the heme formed by erythrocyte heme synthetase is bound to protein and/or lipid. The bound porphyrins found by Porra and Falk (1963) in their studies of coproporphyrinogen oxidase may be related to these possible intermediates in heme synthesis.

3–3 TETRAPYRROLES AS GROWTH FACTORS FOR MICROORGANISMS

Some microorganisms do not grow unless the medium is supplemented with hemin or, in some cases, with precursors (Table 3–1). They therefore lack some part of the complex of enzymes required to elaborate the complete heme molecule, but so far there is little information about the missing enzyme(s) in any of the exacting organisms.

The requirement of *Hemophilus influenzae* for a factor in blood was one of the earliest observations in bacterial nutrition. Later work showed that hemin is required by this organism; the low concentration at which it is effective (about 0.1 μm-mole/ml) is of the same order as that observed with other hemin-requiring micro-

Table 3–1   Microorganisms requiring hemin for growth[a]

Organism	Compounds that replace hemin
Hemophilus influenzae	Protoporphyrin; iron hemato-, deutero-, and mesoporphyrins
Staphylococcus aureus var 511 (*streptomycin-resistant*)	Iron hemato-, deutero-, and mesoporphyrins; heme *a*
Escherichia coli mutants (*streptomycin-resistant*)	Protoporphyrin
Bacteroides spp.	Proto-, hemato-, deutero-, and mesoporphyrins; uro- and coproporphyrinogen III
Physarum polycephalum	Hemoproteins
Trypanosomes (some)	Protoporphyrin

[a] Full references are given in Lascelles (1962b).

organisms (Granick and Gilder, 1947). Protoporphyrin is just as active but other porphyrins are ineffective.

Since protoporphyrin is effective, *H. influenzae* presumably fails at some stage in the formation of protoporphyrin but has heme synthetase. Some strains of *Hemophilus,* however, do not respond to protoporphyrin but only to hemin and therefore apparently lack heme synthetase. This has been confirmed ingeniously by showing that the ability to respond to protoporphyrin is conferred on these strains by transformation with DNA prepared from a strain that grows on either hemin or the porphyrin (White and Granick, 1963).

It seems that hemin-dependent species of *Hemophilus* lack several other enzymes in the biosynthetic pathway to protoporphyrin. Extracts do not utilize ALA, PBG, uro- and coproporphyrinogens, whereas preparations from hemin-independent species convert ALA to a mixture of all these intermediates, showing that the necessary enzymes are present (White and Granick, 1963).

Many of the parasitic flagellates need hemin for growth and presumably, like *H. influenzae,* lack enzymes in the pathway to protoporphyrin since this compound (although not other porphyrins) promotes growth in place of hemin.

The mutant strain of *Staphylococcus aureus* var 511, discovered by Jensen and Thofern (1953), apparently lacks heme synthetase, since it responds to hemin but not to protoporphyrin. Evidence that it has at least some of the enzymes for the pathway to protoporphyrin is shown by its ability to convert ALA to uro- and coproporphyrins (Jensen, 1962). Heme *a* has been demonstrated in the mutant *Staphylococcus* grown on hemin; also heme *a* replaces hemin for growth. Thus, the organism can convert hemin to heme *a* and vice versa (Thofern, 1961). These observations call for deeper analysis at an enzymic level. It is interesting that the mutant *Staphylococcus* is streptomycin-resistant, unlike the parent organism, which is sensitive to the drug and does not need hemin. There seems to be correlation between streptomycin resistance and hemin requirement, since streptomycin-resistant strains of *Escherichia coli* have also been found to require hemin (Table 3–1).

Recently, a number of *Bacteriodes* spp., the predominant bacteria in rumen fluid, have been shown to need hemin for growth (Bryant and Robinson, 1962). These organisms respond to protoporphyrin, but unlike other microorganisms needing hemin, they can also use other porphyrins as well as uro- and coproporphyrinogen III. Presumably in the rumen these bacteria make use of tetrapyrroles formed by the decomposition of chlorophyll ingested by the host animal, although the ability of the *Bacteroides* spp. to use chlorophyll breakdown products has not been demonstrated.

The plasmodial myxomycete *Physarum polycephalum* responds to the hemoproteins, hemoglobin, myoglobin, catalase, peroxidase, and cytochrome *c* (Daniel, Kelley, and Rusch, 1962). These are about ten times more active on a heme basis than is free hemin and exert their effect even when the protein is denatured. It is possible that the organism has enzymes for degrading the proteins, thereby liberating the prosthetic group.

Activity of iron complexes other than protoheme. Curiously, iron complexes of hemato-, meso-, and deuteroporphyrin replace hemin as growth factor for *Hemophilus* and also for some other heminrequiring bacteria. Their activity is not due to conversion to protoheme, since organisms grown with the "abnormal" compounds fail to reduce nitrate, a property found only in cells grown with protoheme (Granick and Gilder, 1947). Presumably, however, they can be incorporated into some hemoproteins without causing complete loss of function. Evidence for a lack of specificity with respect to the prosthetic group has been provided by in vitro studies with *Pseudomonas* cytochrome oxidase (containing heme a_2); when cleaved into the protein and heme a_2 moieties, reconstitution of enzyme activity occurs with other hemes, although heme a_2 gives the highest activity (Yamanaka and Okunuki, 1963).

3–4 IRON-BINDING GROWTH FACTORS

Iron complexes of trihydroxamic acid have recently been identified as growth-promoting factors for some molds and bacteria (Neilands, 1957; Zähner, Bachmann, Hütter, and Nüesch, 1962). Most of the organisms exhibiting this requirement respond to hemin in place of these factors, although it is much less effective. The iron-binding growth factors are collectively known as sideramines and have been detected in cultures of a large number of nonexacting microorganisms (Burnham and Neilands, 1961; Zähner et al., 1962). Several of these factors have been isolated, including ferrichrome from *Ustilago sphaerogenes*, coprogen from a strain of *Penicillium*, and various ferrioxamines from Actinomycetes. The structures of some of the ferrioxamines (Zähner et al., 1962) and of ferrichrome have been determined (Emery and Neilands, 1961); they differ in the way in which the three chelating groups are linked to give a hexadentate-ligand system (Figure 3–5). The sideramines bind ferric iron strongly; upon reduction the iron is readily released.

Since these compounds are growth factors for some microorganisms, they clearly have a biological role. They may function primarily in the transport of iron from the external medium into the cell or in the insertion of iron into the tetrapyrrole nucleus and/or into nonheme iron proteins. Work with a strain of *Arthrobacter* JG9 supports the latter possibilities (Burnham, 1962). This organism requires either ferrichrome or hemin for growth. Cells grown with or without ferrichrome (in the presence of hemin) take up Fe^{59} from the medium with equal facility; this observation seems to indicate ferrichrome is not needed solely to transport iron across the cell membrane. The evidence that it participates in heme synthesis may be summarized as follows:

1. Hemin replaces ferrichrome as a growth factor for *Arthrobacter* JG9 (Burnham, 1962).

2. Addition of ferrichrome to deficient cells of the same organism results in a substantial increase in catalase activity (Burnham and Neilands, 1961).

3. Hemin represses the incorporation of Fe^{59}-labeled ferrichrome by *Arthrobacter* JG9 (Burnham, 1962).

4. Cell-free extracts of *R. spheroides* form labeled heme when incubated with protoporphyrin and Fe^{59} ferrichrome as sole source of iron (Burnham, 1963).

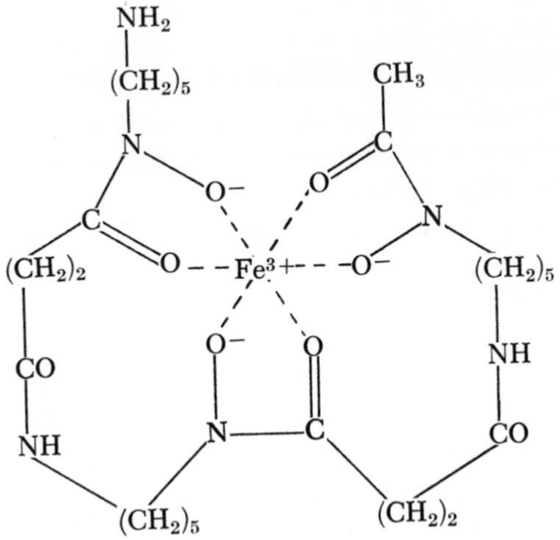

ferrioxamin B

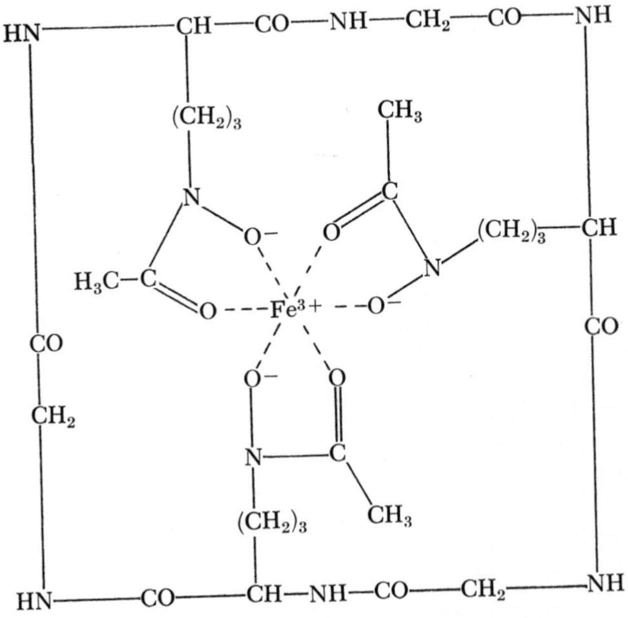

ferrichrome

Figure 3–5   The structure of the iron-binding growth factors, ferrioxamine B, and ferrichrome.

These observations with whole cells and crude extracts show that the iron of ferrichrome can be utilized for heme synthesis. Its function could be to transport iron within the cell to the actual site of synthesis where the iron could then be released upon reduction to the ferrous form. Alternatively, it could serve as a specific donor of iron to the heme synthetase enzyme system as follows:

$$\text{protoporphyrin} + \text{ferrichrome} \xrightarrow[\text{agent}]{\text{reducing}} \text{heme} + \text{apo-ferrichrome}$$

$$\text{apo-ferrichrome} + Fe^{3+} \rightarrow \text{ferrichrome}$$

Purification of microbial systems catalyzing heme formation is required to distinguish between these possibilities.

3–5 FORMATION OF HEMOPROTEINS

The ultimate end of the elaborate series of reactions outlined in Scheme 3–1 is to provide the prosthetic groups for hemoproteins. In living cells, the biosynthesis of heme, requiring the collaboration of mitochondrial and soluble enzymes, keeps in step with the formation of the specific proteins, which are manufactured on the ribosomes. How this complex integration is achieved is unknown.

The formation of hemoproteins has been studied mostly in systems forming hemoglobin and cytochrome c. This is not surprising since these hemoproteins are readily recognized and purified; to study the synthesis of a hemoprotein by isotopic techniques it is essential to isolate the pure substance free from other proteins.

Hemoglobin Synthesis. In early studies of heme biosynthesis by red cell preparations, glycine was shown to be incorporated into globin as well as into the heme. More recently formation of globin and heme, measured by incorporation of C^{14}-glycine, has been followed with suspensions of rabbit bone marrow cells (Morell, Savoie, and London, 1958). Synthesis of both components occurs at parallel rates (Figure 3–6), but the two processes are not interdependent and can be dissociated. Thus, cobaltous ions suppress heme synthesis while globin formation continues and is even slightly enhanced (Figure 3–7).

Synthesis of hemoglobin has been achieved with purified preparations of heme synthetase (from avian erythrocytes) incubated anaerobically with globin, ferrous iron, protoporphyrin, and cysteine (Schwarz, Goudsmit, Hill, Cartwright, and Wintrobe, 1961; Sugita, Yoneyama, and Ohyama, 1962). Substitution of globin by

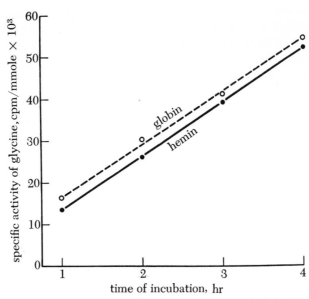

Figure 3–6   Incorporation of C^{14}-glycine into heme and globin by bone marrow suspensions (from Morell et al., 1958).

apo-myoglobin results in the formation of myoglobin (Yoneyama, Ohyama, Sugita, and Yoshikawa, 1963). The experiments do not distinguish between two possible reaction sequences:

1. Synthesis of free heme followed by combination with globin:

$$\text{protoporphyrin} + Fe^{2+} \xrightarrow{\text{heme synthetase}} \text{heme}$$
$$\downarrow \text{globin}$$
$$\text{hemoglobin}$$

2. Combination of protoporphyrin with globin to give a globin-protoporphyrin complex, which in turn reacts with iron under the influence of heme synthetase (Eriksen, 1955):

$$\text{protoporphyrin} + \text{globin} \rightarrow [\text{protoporphyrin-globin}]$$
$$\downarrow \begin{smallmatrix}\text{Fe}\\\text{heme synthetase}\end{smallmatrix}$$
$$\text{hemoglobin}$$

The second possibility is supported by the facts that (1) globin increases heme synthesis by preparations of heme synthetase

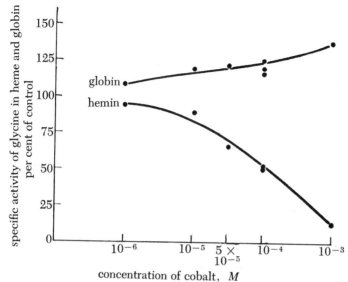

Figure 3–7   Effect of cobaltous ions on glycine incorporation into heme and globin by bone marrow suspensions (from Morell et al., 1958).

(Schwarz et al., 1961); (2) protein-bound protoporphyrin (formed from ALA) is incorporated into heme in preference to free protoporphyrin by duck hemolysates (Sugita, 1962).

Cytochrome c Synthesis. Upon administration of labeled glycine to rats the cytochrome c in the liver, kidney, and skeletal muscle becomes labeled in both the protein and heme moieties; this indicates that all these tissues are capable of forming the cytochrome independently (Marsh and Drabkin, 1957). This is confirmed by similar findings with tissue slices. In these experiments the labeled glycine was initially incorporated into the protein component at a greater rate than into the cytochrome c heme. This may not mean that the two components are formed at different rates but may merely reflect differences in the separate pools of the immediate precursors of the heme and protein components of cytochrome c.

Anaerobically-grown yeast contains no cytochrome c (detected spectroscopically) but synthesizes it when exposed to oxygen (Slonimski, 1956; see Chapter 5). Yčas and Drabkin (1957) have used this system to follow glycine incorporation into cytochrome c. Uptake of labeled glycine into cytochrome c is oxygen-dependent and, as found with animal preparations, the protein component becomes more highly labeled than the heme moiety. This could be due to heme transfer from cytochrome a_1 and b_1, originally present in the organisms before exposure to oxygen, but there is no further evidence to support this.

Bacteria Requiring Hemin for Growth. Microorganisms requiring hemin for growth have not yet been fully exploited to study hemoprotein synthesis. They should provide good experimental systems, since it is possible to regulate the level of preformed hemoprotein by growing the organisms with graded amounts of hemin.

The hemin-requiring mutant of *Staphylococcus aureus* var 511 can be grown in the complete absence of hemin provided the medium is supplemented with acetate and uracil (Jensen and Thofern, 1953; Lascelles, 1956b; Gardner and Lascelles, 1962). When grown in this way the cells are devoid of cytochromes, whereas those grown with hemin have the absorption bands typical of cytochromes b_1 and a. The hemin-free cells do not respire nor do they have catalase and nitrate reductase activity. Upon addition of hemin to the washed cells, in the presence of only buffer and glucose, these activities are immediately exhibited. This suggests that the organisms make the various apoenzymes when grown without hemin and are able to incorporate added hemin to give fully functional hemoproteins. Iron porphyrins other than hemin do not activate the washed cells, although they promote growth (Thofern, 1961). Direct evidence for the presence of specific protein components in cells grown without hemin has been provided by observations with cell-free extracts (Chang and Lascelles, 1963). Upon addition of hemin to such extracts, cytochrome b_1 is formed, shown both by spectroscopy and by the activation of nitrate reductase; other iron porphyrins are inactive. The "apocytochrome" is located in the particulate fraction of the extracts.

Reconstitution of the hemoprotein, catalase, has been shown by addition of hemin to extracts of the streptomycin-resistant strain of *Escherichia coli* that requires hemin for growth. Proto- and hemato-porphyrin inhibit the activation, possibly by competing with hemin for the combining sites on the apoenzyme (Beljanski and Beljanski, 1957).

The fact that these mutant organisms apparently form the protein components of various hemoproteins in the absence of the prosthetic group shows that synthesis of the proteins occurs quite independently of the heme component. Purification of the various protein moieties should lead to an understanding of how the prosthetic group becomes incorporated into the protein structure to give the various specific hemoproteins.

3–6   DISTRIBUTION OF ENZYMES
CONCERNED IN TETRAPYRROLE SYNTHESIS:
SOURCES OF PRIMARY PRECURSORS

General Distribution of Enzymes. Since hemoglobin is by far the major tetrapyrrole-containing compound in animals, it is to be expected that the tissues responsible for forming this pigment contain the highest concentration of enzymes needed for its synthesis. All the enzymic steps have been demonstrated in avian erythrocytes (Table 3–2) and because of their ready availability these cells have

Table 3–2   Distribution of enzymes concerned in heme synthesis

Enzymic step	Distribution	Intracellular localization, animal tissues
ALA synthetase	Avian erythrocytes; liver; photosynthetic bacteria	Mitochondria
ALA dehydratase	Avian erythrocytes; widespread in animal tissues, particularly liver, kidney, and bone marrow; photosynthetic and other bacteria	Cytoplasm
PBG → uroporphyrinogen III	Avian erythrocytes; plant tissues; photosynthetic bacteria	Cytoplasm
Uroporphyrinogen III → coproporphyrinogen III	Avian erythrocytes; plant tissues; photosynthetic bacteria	Cytoplasm
Coproporphyrinogen III → protoporphyrin	Avian erythrocytes; widespread in animal tissues, particularly liver; algae	Mitochondria
Heme synthetase	Avian erythrocytes; liver; heart muscle; yeast; photosynthetic and other bacteria	Mitochondria

been a popular source of enzymes for purification studies. The major site of hemoglobin synthesis in mammals, the bone marrow, has not been widely used, undoubtedly because of the difficulty of obtaining large quantities of the material.

All cells that contain cytochromes and catalase can be presumed to have the enzymes for heme formation. Most of these enzymes have been shown in various animal tissues, particularly liver (Table 3–2). Correlations have yet to be made between the cytochrome and catalase content of tissues and the activity of the enzymes required for heme biosynthesis. Liver is rich in catalase and the relatively high activity of the enzymes in this tissue may be related more to the formation of catalase than to cytochromes, since the available data suggest that tissues with a higher cytochrome content than liver are considerably less active with respect to the biosynthetic enzymes. For instance, the ALA dehydratase and coproporphyrinogen oxidase activity of rabbit heart muscle are, respectively, about one-thirtieth and one-tenth that of liver (Gibson et al., 1955; Sano and Granick, 1961). The correlation between catalase activity and the level of the biosynthetic enzymes is also suggested by the diminished catalase content of livers from Sedormid-treated animals; this drug interferes in some way with the control of tetrapyrrole formation and causes porphyria (Schmid, Figen, and Schwartz, 1955).

Pre-eminent of the bacteria examined for enzymes of the tetrapyrrole path are the photosynthetic ones, particularly of the Athiorhodaceae family. This reflects the fact that these organisms have by far the highest concentration of tetrapyrroles in the form of chlorophyll. It is surprising, however, that ALA synthetase has so far been demonstrated only in the Athiorhodaceae although ALA dehydratase is readily detectable in both photosynthetic and nonphotosynthetic bacteria; this probably is due to deficiencies in the assay techniques rather than to lack of enzyme.

Intracellular Localization of Enzymes. It is interesting to note that in animal tissues the enzymes concerned in the initial stage (ALA synthetase) and the final stages (coproporphyrinogen III to heme) are located in the mitochondria whereas intermediate steps are catalyzed by cytoplasmic enzymes (Table 3–2). This partitioning of the enzymes within the cell may contribute to the control of tetrapyrrole formation (see Chapter 5). In the photosynthetic bacteria the enzymes concerned in the stages to coproporphyrinogen III are in the soluble fraction of the cells, but heme synthetase is in the particulate fraction (R. J. Porra, personal communication).

Origin of the Primary Precursors. In considering tetrapyrrole synthesis by the pathway shown in Scheme 3–1 the source of the primary substrates, glycine and succinyl CoA, must be taken into account.

Glycine. In animals most of this amino acid probably comes from dietary sources. It can also arise from serine by the reaction catalyzed by serine hydroxymethyltransferase:

serine + tetrahydrofolic acid $\rightleftharpoons$ glycine + N^{10}-hydroxymethyltetrahydrofolic acid

The serine is in turn derived from 3-phosphoglycerate as shown in Scheme 3–3 (Greenberg, 1961; Umbarger and Davis, 1962).

In bacteria such as *Escherichia coli*, growing on glucose and ammonia, glycine is probably formed mainly by the same series of reactions; the origin of serine from 3-phosphoglycerate via phosphohydroxypyruvate and phosphoserine has now been definitely established (Umbarger, Umbarger, and Siu, 1963; Pizer, 1963). The existence of a similar pathway in photosynthetic bacteria has not been investigated. In these organisms glyoxylate may be an important precursor. An enzyme which catalyzes the cleavage of malate to glyoxylate has been shown in *Rhodospirillum rubrum* (Stern, 1963).

malate + ATP + CoA $\rightleftharpoons$ acetyl CoA + glyoxylate

In plants, glyoxylate may also be a major precursor of glycine; both are early products of CO_2 fixation by algae and leaf tissue (Bassham and Calvin, 1957; Davies, 1959).

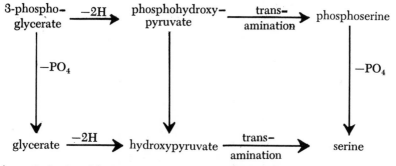

Scheme 3–3   Possible reactions in the conversion of phosphoglycerate to serine.

Table 3–3 Enzyme reactions producing succinyl CoA

Enzyme system	Reaction catalyzed	Cofactors
α-Ketoglutarate oxidase	α-Ketoglutarate → succinyl CoA + CO_2 + $NADH_2$	Thiamine pyrophosphate; lipoic acid, NAD, CoA
Succinyl CoA synthetase	Succinate + nucleotide triphosphate + CoA ⇌ succinyl CoA + nucleotide diphosphate + Pi	GTP (animals); ATP (bacteria, plants)
Acetoacetyl CoA transferase[a]	Succinate + acetoacetyl CoA ⇌ succinyl CoA + acetoacetate	
Methylmalonyl CoA isomerase	Methylmalonyl CoA ⇌ succinyl CoA	B_{12} coenzyme

[a] Other transferases are also known.

64

Succinyl CoA. This compound is a product of several enzyme reactions but it seems likely that its major source, at least in animal tissues, is by oxidative decarboxylation of α-ketoglutarate (Table 3–3).

Production of succinyl CoA either directly from succinate or from α-ketoglutarate implies the operation, at least in part, of the tricarboxylic acid cycle. This cycle might therefore be expected to operate in tissues and organisms that form tetrapyrroles and, on the whole, the evidence fits this presumption. It has been shown in avian erythrocytes although not in mature mammalian red cells that do not form heme (London, 1961). The localization of the cycle in mitochondria accords with the localization of ALA synthetase in this cell fraction. In microorganisms there is quite good correlation between the ability to form tetrapyrroles and the presence of at least some reactions of the cycle (Table 3–4). In particular, it is interesting to note that members of the lactobacillus group lack cytochromes and catalase as well as the tricarboxylic acid cycle, whereas the strongly fermentative propionibacteria form these hemoproteins and have enzymes of the cycle. There are, however, a few anomalous organisms in which the cycle cannot be

Table 3–4   The occurrence of tetrapyrroles and the tricarboxylic acid cycle in microorganisms[a]

Organism	Major tetrapyrroles formed	Tricarboxylic acid cycle
Yeast	Cytochromes	+
Photosynthetic bacteria (Athio- and Thiorhodaceae)	Bacteriochlorophyll, cytochromes, porphyrins	+
Coryne. erythrogenes	Cytochromes, porphyrins	+
Prop. shermanii	Cytochromes, porphyrins	+
B. subtilis	Cytochromes, porphyrins	+
Micro. lysodeikticus	Cytochromes, porphyrins	+
Azotobacter spp.	Cytochromes	+
Desulpho. desulphuricans	Cytochromes	+
Lactobacilli	Nil	−
Clostridia spp.	Nil[b]	−

[a] In most of the organisms listed, only some of the individual steps of the cycle have been shown; the ability to oxidize dicarboxylic acids to CO_2 is taken as evidence for the operation of the cycle (Kornberg, 1959).
[b] Some *Clostridia* are rich in vitamin B_{12} coenzymes.

demonstrated although they can form hemes (Lascelles, 1962b). These include some species of *Acetobacter* that lack key enzymes of the cycle including α-ketoglutarate oxidase.

Among the strictly anaerobic *Clostridia* there are some which form considerable amounts of vitamin B_{12} derivatives (Barker, 1961; Stadtman, 1960) although the tricarboxylic acid cycle has not been shown in organisms of this group. If ALA is a precursor, as it is in other microorganisms (Bray and Shemin, 1963), the problem of the origin of succinyl CoA, required for ALA synthesis, is again raised. It is possible that a major source is from succinate via the succinyl-CoA-synthetase reaction; the succinate could arise by reduction of fumarate.

4

THE BIOSYNTHESIS
OF TETRAPYRROLES:
PATHWAY TO CHLOROPHYLLS

4–1 STAGES TO PROTOPORPHYRIN

The work of Granick and colleagues with mutant strains of the
unicellular alga, *Chlorella*, was the first indication that the early
steps of heme and chlorophyll synthesis share a common pathway
that branches at the stage of protoporphyrin. The mutant strains,
produced by irradiation with X rays, were blocked at stages in the
biosynthesis of chlorophyll but were capable of heterotrophic
growth on glucose. The first to be described accumulated massive
amounts of protoporphyrin in the cells suggesting that this porphyrin was a precursor of chlorophyll (Granick, 1948a). Re-irradia-
tion of this strain produced another mutant that accumulated a
mixture of porphyrins with two to eight carboxyl groups, dicarboxylic porphyrins being predominant (Bogorad and Granick,
1953a). Protoporphyrin, uro- and coproporphyrin III, hematoporphyrin IX and monovinylmonoethyldeuteroporphyrin IX were
identified in these mixtures (Granick, Bogorad, and Jaffe, 1953).
The accumulation of uro- and coproporphyrins can be expected
from what is now known of the steps leading to protoporphyrin
(Scheme 3–1). The occurrence of the latter two porphyrins does

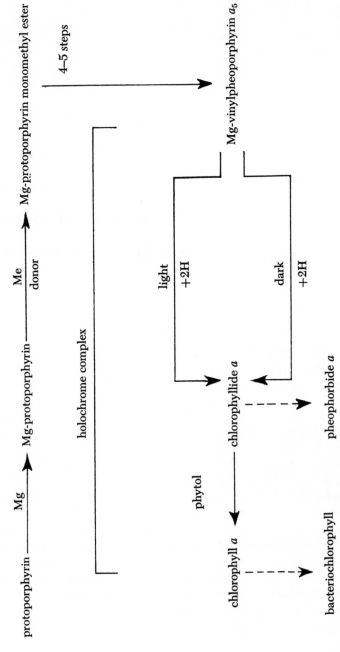

Scheme 4–1   The path of chlorophyll synthesis.

not however fit in with current views of protoporphyrin synthesis; they may arise by spontaneous degradation of true intermediates (Bogorad, 1962).

The accumulation of porphyrins by the mutants provided evidence that chlorophyll was formed by a pathway involving these substances (or their corresponding porphyrinogens) but did not indicate whether the tetrapyrrole structure was formed by the biosynthetic pathway used by animals. Evidence for this came from other methods of approach: (1) C^{14}-labeled glycine and acetate were incorporated into chlorophyll by cultures of *Chlorella* to give the distribution pattern to be expected if the path outlined in Scheme 3–1 operated (Della Rosa, Altman, and Salomon, 1953). (2) Preparations of *Chlorella* converted ALA and PBG to a mixture of porphyrins, in which uro- and coproporphyrins predominated (Granick, 1954; Bogorad and Granick, 1953b). (3) The isolation from plant tissues of enzyme fractions catalyzing the conversion of PBG to uroporphyrinogen III was achieved (Bogorad, 1958a, b).

The synthesis of bacteriochlorophyll by photosynthetic bacteria also occurs by the usual pathway, as shown by the accumulation of porphyrins in the presence of glycine and succinate and by the isolation of enzymes catalyzing individual steps in the pathway to protoporphyrin (Lascelles, 1962b).

4–2 PATHWAY FROM PROTOPORPHYRIN TO CHLOROPHYLLS

The steps between protoporphyrin and the chlorophylls are largely unknown, and Scheme 4–1, which summarizes the present situation, is only slightly more advanced than that originally proposed by Granick (1950a). The available information about intermediates has come mainly from the isolation of presumed chlorophyll precursors accumulated by mutant strains of algae and photosynthetic bacteria which are unable to form chlorophyll (Table 4–1).

Steps to Magnesium Vinylpheoporphyrin a_5. The three magnesium-containing compounds that have been isolated from mutant strains of *Chlorella* are Mg-protoporphyrin, Mg-protoporphyrin monomethylester, and Mg-vinylpheoporphyrin a_5 (Figure 4–1). The formation of each of these will now be considered.

Magnesium protoporphyrin. This compound was found by Granick (1948b) to be accumulated by a *Chlorella* mutant. This ob-

Table 4–1   Chlorophyll derivatives accumulated by photosynthetic microorganisms

Compound	Accumulated by
Mg-protoporphyrin	*Chlorella* mutant
Mg-protoporphyrin monomethylester	*Chlorella* mutant *R. spheroides* *R. capsulata*
Mg-vinylpheoporphyrin a_5 (MgVP; protochlorophyllide *a*)	*Chlorella* mutant
Mg-2,4-divinylpheoporphyrin a_5 and other MgVP-type compounds	*R. spheroides* mutants (and wild-type under some conditions)
Pheophorbide *a* 2-Desvinyl-2-hydroxyethyl pheophorbide *a*	

servation suggested that the magnesium of the chlorophylls is incorporated at a relatively early stage in the biosynthetic sequence. Nothing is known of the mechanism by which the metal complex is formed from protoporphyrin. The reaction is almost certainly enzyme-catalyzed. The free porphyrin and the magnesium derivative are accumulated by different mutants, suggesting that the strain forming the free porphyrin lacks the enzyme for insertion of the metal.

Magnesium protoporphyrin monomethylester. Both protoporphyrin monomethylester and the magnesium derivative are accumulated by another mutant of *Chlorella* (Granick, 1961b). It is not definitely established whether the propionic acid sidechain on C atom 6 or 7 of the porphin nucleus is esterified but inspection of the structure of chlorophyll makes it reasonable to assume that it is the sidechain on C-6. The magnesium ester has also been identified in culture filtrates of the photosynthetic bacteria *R. spheroides* (Jones, 1963a) and *R. capsulata* (Cooper, 1963). The latter organism accumulates the compound in large amounts when incubated with glycine, succinate, and methionine.

There is now considerable information about the way in which magnesium protoporphyrin monomethylester is formed. The specific incorporation of C^{14}-formate by *Chlorella* into the methyl ester group of chlorophyll was the first indication that this group is derived from a one-carbon unit (Green, Altman, Richmond, and

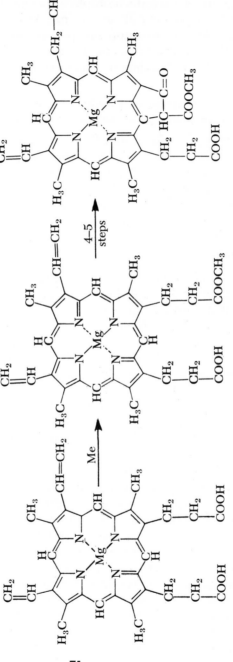

Mg-protoporphyrin   Mg-protoporphyrin monomethyl ester   Mg vinylpheoporphyrin a_5

Figure 4-1 Mg-protoporphyrin, Mg-protoporphyrin monomethyl ester and magnesium vinylpheoporphyrin a_5.

71

Salomon, 1957). In *R. spheroides*, 1-C^{14}-methionine labels the methyl group of bacteriochlorophyll specifically and this observation has been pursued at an enzymic level (Gibson, Neuberger, and Tait, 1963). Chromatophore preparations from the organism catalyze the following reaction, the responsible enzyme being designated S-adenosylmethionine-magnesium protoporphyrin methyltransferase:

magnesium protoporphyrin + S-adenosylmethionine →

magnesium protoporphyrin monomethylester + S-adenosylhomocysteine

The enzyme is confined and firmly bound to the chromatophore fraction of the cells. Free protoporphyrin is not utilized but other metal porphyrins besides the magnesium complex are active. S-adenosylethionine inhibits the enzyme competitively and this accounts for previous observations by the same workers that ethionine inhibits bacteriochlorophyll synthesis by whole cells.

This step is the only one in chlorophyll biosynthesis (after protoporphyrin) to be studied so far at an enzymic level.

Magnesium vinyl pheoporphyrin a₅ *(MgVP)*. This compound, also known as protochlorophyllide *a*, is accumulated by a *Chlorella* mutant that forms chlorophyll only upon illumination, whereas normal strains form chlorophyll in both light and dark (Granick, 1950b). MgVP also exists in a protein-bound form in etiolated leaves (i.e., leaves deprived of light) and is responsible for their pale green color. The combination of pigment with protein has been termed "holochrome" by Smith (1963) and the MgVP-holochrome is probably the true intermediate in chlorophyll synthesis rather than the free pigment (see below).

Free MgVP is formed in the dark from ALA by etiolated leaves (Granick, 1961b). Presumably the conversion proceeds via magnesium protoporphyrin monomethylester but the steps after this compound are completely unknown. The following changes in the structure of the monomethylester are required to form MgVP: (1) reduction of the vinyl sidechain on C-4 of the porphin nucleus to ethyl; (2) oxidation of the $-CH_2 \cdot CH_2 \cdot CO \cdot OCH_3$ sidechain on C-6 to $-CO-CH_2 CO \cdot OCH_3$; (3) cyclization of this sidechain to give the cyclopentanone ring. Granick (1963a) has suggested that four enzymic steps are required for the conversion.

Pigments closely resembling MgVP in absorption spectra and solubility are excreted by mutants of *R. spheroides* unable to form bacteriochlorophyll (Stanier and Smith, 1959; Griffiths, 1962). They are also accumulated by the wild-type organism when grown in the presence of 8-hydroxyquinoline (Jones, 1963b). The slight differences in absorption spectra suggest that the bacterial pigments differ from MgVP only in the nature of the sidechains on C-2 or C-4 of the porphin nucleus. This is confirmed by the identification of one of these compounds as 2,4-divinylpheoporphyrin a_5 (Jones, 1963c). The divinyl compound could well be a precursor of MgVP and the synthesis of the bacterial and plant chlorophylls may therefore follow the same path at least to the stage of MgVP.

Final Stages. The steps from MgVP to chlorophyll *a* involve reduction of pyrrole ring D of the porphin nucleus followed by esterification of the propionic sidechain on C-7 with phytol. The intermediates in these reactions are very probably protein-bound and to add to the complexity the reduction occurs only in the light in higher plants and in some algae.

The reduction step in higher plants and algae. The light-induced synthesis of chlorophyll by dark-grown seedlings has been studied in detail by Smith and co-workers at the Stanford Laboratory of the Carnegie Institute.

Seedlings that have developed in the dark contain protein-bound MgVP but not chlorophyll. Upon illumination the spectrum of the MgVP complex is transformed rapidly to that of chlorophyll *a*. Action spectra measurements show that light of the wavelengths absorbed by the bound MgVP is the most effective in bringing about the transformation.

Protein fractions ("protochlorophyll(ide) holochrome") with a molecular weight of about 700,000 have been isolated from dark-grown seedlings; these contain MgVP in its active form (Smith, 1960; 1963; Granick, 1963a). The MgVP of the holochrome has an absorption maximum at 650 mμ and is converted by light to chlorophyllide, whereas free MgVP absorbs maximally at 631 mμ and is bleached by light. It appears that the isolated MgVP-holochrome contains the bound form of MgVP, which is the true intermediate in chlorophyll *a* synthesis in higher plants. The nature of the reducing component that is generated by light is unknown; the holochrome presumably has an enzyme(s) for carrying out the reduction.

The stage at which free intermediates in the biosynthetic sequence become incorporated into the holochrome complex is not known. Free MgVP is not incorporated. This is shown by the observation that MgVP accumulated from ALA in the dark by etiolated barley leaves is not converted to chlorophyll upon subsequent illumination. Chlorophyll is, however, formed from endogenous precursors upon illumination and proceeds independently of the MgVP formed from ALA (Granick, 1963a).

Most of the simple algae form chlorophyll in the dark as well as in the light. They must therefore have enzyme systems which reduce MgVP, probably in protein-bound form, to the chlorophyllide. A separate enzyme system is presumably involved in the light-dependent and light-independent reactions since mutant strains of algae have been isolated that differ from the parent organisms in being able to synthesize chlorophyll only in the light (Granick, 1950b; Sager, 1959).

The reductive step in photosynthetic bacteria. Bacteriochlorophyll synthesis has been studied only in photosynthetic bacteria of the Athiorhodaceae group. Most of these organisms can grow either anaerobically in the light or aerobically in the dark. Under the latter conditions bacteriochlorophyll is synthesized provided that the oxygen tension is low (Lascelles, 1959). These organisms must therefore have enzyme systems capable of catalyzing the reduction of rings B and D of the porphin nucleus in the dark. Nothing is known of these systems. Compounds which resemble MgVP and pheophorbide *a* (Figure 4–2) in solubility and absorp-

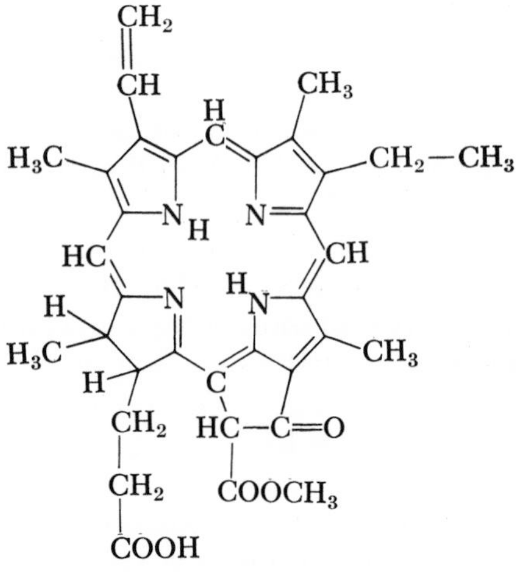

pheophorbide *a*

Figure 4–2   Pheophorbide a.

tion spectrum accumulate in cultures of *R. spheroides* under certain conditions (Sistrom, Griffiths, and Stanier, 1956; Jones, 1963b, c, 1964; Lascelles, 1963; see Table 4–1). This suggests that reduction of ring D to give the dihydrotetrapyrrole structure of the plant chlorophylls precedes the reduction of ring B. The absence of magnesium from the accumulated pheophorbides is probably due to spontaneous decomposition. A study of the synthesis of these compounds could throw light on the mechanism of reduction of the pyrrole rings.

It is not known whether the precursors of bacteriochlorophyll are protein-bound. The fact that compounds similar to MgVP accumulate in the culture medium of mutants does not preclude this possibility, since free MgVP is accumulated by *Chlorella* mutants and by etiolated leaves (from ALA) although the true intermediate seems to be protein-bound.

Esterification with phytol. The evidence that esterification of the propionic sidechain on C-7 of the porphin nucleus occurs after reduction of the pyrrole ring in the synthesis of chlorophyll *a* may be summarized as follows:

1. Transformation of MgVP to chlorophyll *a* in etiolated leaves has been separated into a photochemical and a dark, enzymic reaction (Wolff and Price, 1957). Analysis of the pigments, based on solubility in organic solvents and chromatography, after 10 seconds' exposure to red light showed that chlorophyllide *a* had been formed but little chlorophyll *a*. When the brief illumination was followed by incubation in the dark, there was a steady increase in chlorophyll *a*, the rate being dependent on temperature. These observations suggest the following sequence:

$$\text{MgVP} \xrightarrow[+2\text{H}]{\text{light}} \text{chlorophyllide } a$$
$$\text{phytol} \downarrow \text{dark}$$
$$\text{chlorophyll } a$$

2. The isolated MgVP holochrome contains no phytylated compounds (Smith, 1961).

3. *R. spheroides* accumulates pheophorbides that are unphytylated.

The mechanism of esterification with phytol is unknown. It has been frequently suggested that the reaction is catalyzed by chlorophyllase. This enzyme is present in leaves and catalyzes the reaction:

$$\text{chlorophyll} \xrightarrow{\text{H}_2\text{O}} \text{chlorophyllide} + \text{phytol}$$

Chlorophyllase acts in concentrations of acetone up to 80 per cent. Its assay in an aqueous system containing the emulsifying agent Tween 80 has been described by Klein and Vishniac (1961). Using this assay the enzyme has been purified 500-fold from etiolated rye seedlings and it appears to be a lipoprotein.

The participation of chlorophyllase in the phytylation step in chlorophyll synthesis is supported by the following: (1) Activity of the enzyme increases upon illumination of etiolated leaves, i.e., increased enzyme is associated with active chlorophyll synthesis (Holden, 1961). (2) Phytol inhibits the breakdown of chlorophyll catalyzed by water-soluble preparations of the enzyme from tobacco leaves (Shimizo and Tamaki, 1963). (3) The same enzyme preparation catalyzes chlorophyll and pheophytin formation, respectively, when incubated with phytol and chlorophyllide or pheophorbide.

The apparent ability of chlorophyllase to catalyze the synthesis and hydrolysis of chlorophyll is similar to the action of cholesterol esterase. Preparations of this enzyme from pancreas bring about the esterification of the sterol with long-chain fatty acids as well as the hydrolysis of cholesterol esters (Hernandez and Chaikoff, 1957). The possibility still remains that at least one substrate must be activated (e.g., as a CoA or phosphate derivative); this would be analogous with other biochemical systems in which esterification of a carboxylic acid group occurs, such as in the formation of the phosphatidic acids (Kennedy, 1961).

Phytol itself is probably formed from C_2 units via mevalonic acid by a pathway similar to that leading to carotenoids and other isoprenoid derivatives (Popjak and Cornforth, 1960). Free phytol has been detected in chloroplasts but is absent from etiolated leaves (Fischer and Bohn, 1957). It appears, therefore, that its formation is geared to that of the tetrapyrrole moiety of the chlorophyll molecule.

Since phytol is highly water-insoluble, the final stage of chlorophyll synthesis may occur in the lipoprotein fraction of the plant chloroplast or the bacterial chromatophore.

Farnesol, which is found in the Chlorobium chlorophylls in place of phytol (see Section 1–1), is presumably formed and esterified with the tetrapyrrole moiety by mechanisms similar to those for phytol.

4–3 CHLOROPLAST AND CHROMATOPHORE STRUCTURE IN RELATION TO CHLOROPHYLL SYNTHESIS

Chloroplasts

Chlorophyll and the lamellar structure. Electron micrographs of the chloroplasts of higher plants and algae show a series of double membrane lamellae (grana lamellae) stacked one on the other (Figure 4–3). These are thought to contain the photosynthetic pigments as well as protein, lipid, and certain enzymes associated with photosynthesis. A model showing the orientation of the various molecules to give the lamellar structure has been proposed by Calvin (1959). This model places chlorophyll with its phytol residue in a central position for the ordering of the final lamellar structure (Figure 4–4). The close association of chlorophyll and the lamellar structure is shown by their simultaneous appearance during the greening of etiolated leaves in response to light (Granick, 1961b, 1963b).

Figure 4–3   Electron micrograph showing chloroplasts of *Elodea* leaf (from Mühlethaler and Frey-Wyssling, 1959).

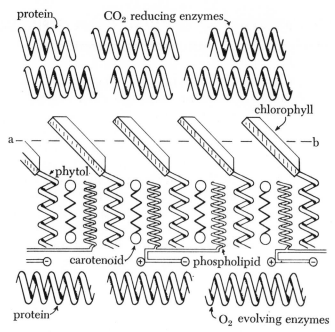

Figure 4–4   Schematic representation of possible molecular structure of lamellae (Calvin, 1959).

The final stages of chlorophyll synthesis are probably intimately connected with the development of the chloroplast lamellae. Evidence for this has been provided by electron microscopy in conjunction with chemical analysis of etiolated leaves exposed to light of varying intensity (Eilam and Klein, 1962; Klein, 1962, Figure 4–5). Low light intensity results in the transformation of MgVP to chlorophyllide, but not to chlorophyll, with concurrent arrangement of the vesicular structures present before illumination into concentric layers. Fusion of these layers to give the lamellar structure typical of the mature chloroplast occurs only upon illumination at higher intensities, which also causes the synthesis of chlorophyll. The conclusion is that phytylation may be a necessary factor in the fusion of vesicles to lamellar structures.

Chloroplast formation by etiolated leaves. In the development of the mature chloroplast upon illumination of etiolated leaves many other events are occurring besides the final elaboration of the

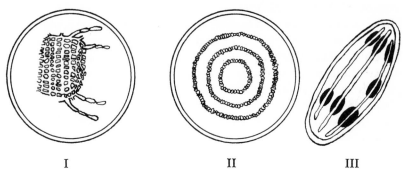

I   II   III

Figure 4–5   Schematic representation of the development of the lamellar structure of chloroplasts. I, 12 days dark; II, 24 hr low light; III, 24 hr high light (from Eilam and Klein, 1962).

chlorophyll molecules and the ordering of the internal structure. These include the synthesis of new proteins and lipids (Granick, 1961b, 1963b; Mego and Jagendorf, 1961). Chloramphenicol inhibits light-induced chlorophyll formation suggesting that its synthesis is obligatorily bound to the synthesis of the new proteins (Margulies, 1962). Actinomycin D is also inhibitory, which points to a requirement for DNA-dependent RNA synthesis in chlorophyll synthesis (Bogorad and Jacobson, 1964).

The proteins formed in response to illumination include enzymes concerned in CO_2 fixation by the reductive pentose cycle and transhydrogenase; these enzymes are absent or present at low levels in dark-grown leaves (Smillie, 1963; Keister, Jagendorf, and San Pietro, 1962). It seems likely that the protein component of the MgVP holochrome (present before illumination) increases during illumination (Kupke, 1962). There is evidence that it is identical with the soluble protein fraction located in the chloroplasts of green leaves and variously designated as the F_1 protein (Lyttleton and Ts'o, 1958) or the 18S protein (Kupke, 1962). This fraction comprises 25 per cent of the dry chloroplast and may be a multienzyme complex containing enzymes of the reductive pentose cycle. Kupke showed that the 18S protein fraction increased on illumination in parallel with the chlorophyll, but the increase in pigment far exceeded that of the protein; a doubling of the latter was accompanied by a thirty- to fortyfold increase in chlorophyll.

All these changes are apparently set in motion by the photoconversion of MgVP holochrome to the chlorophyllide. The chlorophyllide may become detached from the holochrome protein (18S protein?) to become incorporated into the lipoprotein fraction of the chloroplast; this might occur simultaneously with or soon after phytylation of the molecule. The absorption maximum of chlorophyll formed by illumination of etiolated seedlings changes from about 684 to 673 mμ after standing for a short time; this change may be due to reorientation of the molecule upon phytylation (Smith, 1960).

Chloroplast formation in Euglena gracilis. The green flagellate *Euglena gracilis* loses its chlorophyll and chloroplasts when grown in the dark. Incubation of the dark-grown cells in the light with only phosphate, magnesium ions, and glucose results in chlorophyll synthesis and restoration of the chloroplasts (Brawerman and Chargaff, 1959a, b; Smillie, 1963). Chlorophyll synthesis is accompanied by an increase in the protein of the chloroplast fraction of the cells, probably derived largely by turnover of the cytoplasmic protein. The RNA content of the cells also increases, and the newly formed ribosomal RNA has a nucleotide composition that differs from that of the etiolated cells (Brawerman, Pogo, and Chargaff, 1962; Brawerman, 1963). How these changes are triggered by illumination is unknown. The *Euglena* system provides a valuable experimental system for studying the final stages of chlorophyll synthesis and the macromolecular changes that are associated with them.

Chromatophores of Photosynthetic Bacteria. The chlorophyll of photosynthetic bacteria is located in subcellular particles or chromatophores that can be readily separated by differential centrifugation from cell-free extracts, prepared by mechanical or sonic disintegration (Lascelles, 1962a; see Chapter 2). Electron microscopy of sections of pigmented cells has revealed membrane-bound vesicles that correspond in size to the isolated chromatophores, suggesting that the latter arise from the vesicular intracellular structures (Figure 4–6). There is good correlation between the number of vesicles seen in electron micrographs of cell sections and the concentration of bacteriochlorophyll, providing strong evidence that these structures bear the photosynthetic pigments. Thus, *Rhodospirillum rubrum,* grown under low light intensity and therefore rich in bacteriochlorophyll, exhibits many vesicles extending deep into the cytoplasm, whereas far fewer vesicles are evident in sections of cells with a lower pigment content due to growth under high light intensity (Cohen-Bazire and Kunisawa,

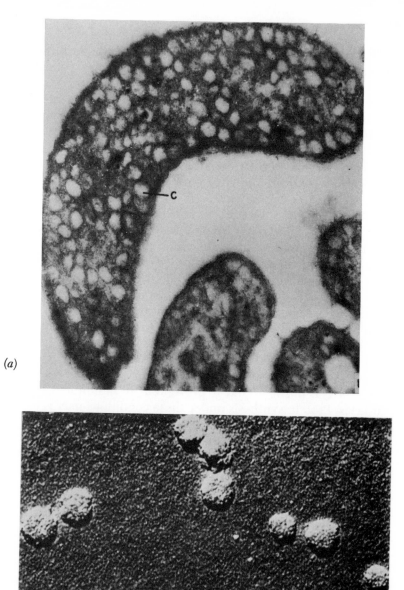

(a)

(b)

Figure 4–6   Electron micrographs showing chromatophores of *Rhodospirillum rubrum*. (a) Section of cell (C = chromatophore); (b) purified preparation (from Hickman and Frenkel, 1959).

1963). In Athiorhodaceae grown aerobically in the dark the intracellular structures are not detectable, and this corresponds to the virtual absence of bacteriochlorophyll.

These presumed pigment-bearing vesicles may arise from or be part of the cytoplasmic membrane. Thus, the photosynthetic pigments are located in the "ghost" (i.e., membrane) fraction of cells which have been lysed by osmotic shock after treatment with lysozyme (Tuttle and Gest, 1959). Also, electron microscopy of sections of *Rsp. rubrum* and *Rsp. molischianum* has shown some of the vesicles to be continuous with the membrane (Cohen-Bazire and Kunisawa, 1963; Giesbrecht and Drews, 1962).

Synthesis of chlorophyll by photosynthetic bacteria may therefore involve considerable modification of the cytoplasmic membrane. Such modifications might be expected to be most marked when Athiorhodaceae are transferred from highly aerobic conditions (which prevent pigment synthesis) to conditions which promote bacteriochlorophyll formation. *R. spheroides* has been used in an experimental system of this type to study the possible relation between pigment-synthesis and chromatophore formation (Bull and Lascelles, 1963). Bacteriochlorophyll synthesis is obligatorily linked to protein synthesis, since it is dependent on a source of cell nitrogen and is prevented by inhibitors of protein synthesis. Protein synthesis under these conditions may represent, at least partly, the formation of the chromatophore structure. This is suggested by the preferential incorporation of labeled amino acids into the chromatophore fraction of the cell protein, which occurs only under conditions that permit simultaneous pigment synthesis. Nothing is known of the stage in the biosynthetic pathway at which biosynthetic intermediates become associated with the intracellular structures.

4–4   IRON AND CHLOROPHYLL SYNTHESIS

In both plants and photosynthetic bacteria iron deficiency has drastic effects on chlorophyll synthesis. Limitation of iron is the most effective method of inducing chlorosis in plants (Rabinowitch, 1945). In the Athiorhodaceae the bacteriochlorophyll content of iron-deficient cells is about one-third or less than that in normal organisms (see Table 2–7).

In iron-deficient plants diminished chlorophyll is accompanied by considerable changes in the lamellar structure of the chloroplasts (Bogorad, Pires, Swift, and McIlrath, 1959). Also, the protein content of the chloroplast fraction of iron-chlorotic leaves is considerably less than in normal leaves, although there is no difference in the protein concentration of the cytoplasmic fraction (Perur, Smith, and Wiebe, 1961).

These observations raise the question of whether the observed effect of iron deficiency on chlorophyll synthesis is the result or the cause of the changes in chloroplast structure. As discussed previously, the final elaboration of the lamellar structure apparently depends on the presence of chlorophyll molecules, so it is to be expected that blockage of chlorophyll synthesis would affect chloroplast structure.

In higher plants iron deficiency may interfere with synthesis of the pigment by preventing synthesis of ALA (Marsh, Evans, and Matrone, 1963a, b; see Section 3–1), and the effects on chloroplast structure could stem from this block.

There is evidence that iron is required for the conversion of coproporphyrinogen to protoporphyrin in photosynthetic bacteria and decreased bacteriochlorophyll synthesis would therefore ensue under conditions of iron deficiency (see Section 3–1). It is not known whether the structure or composition of the chromatophores is altered under these circumstances.

5

THE CONTROL
OF TETRAPYRROLE SYNTHESIS

5–1 MANIFESTATION OF CONTROL MECHANISMS

The steps in the biosynthetic pathway leading to the functional tetrapyrroles are subject to control mechanisms that regulate the supply of intermediates so there is little wastage. This is clearly seen by comparing the concentration of the major tetrapyrrole derivatives in living matter with the concentration of intermediates or porphyrin by-products (Table 5–1). Under normal conditions only traces of ALA, PBG, and porphyrins are found but when the control mechanisms fail intermediates and porphyrins may reach levels considerably higher than those of the functional tetrapyrroles. The high concentrations reached under uncontrolled conditions demonstrate the potential capacity of enzymes of the biosynthetic pathway when allowed to operate freely and emphasize the necessity for regulatory mechanisms in the economy of the organism.

Photosynthetic organisms synthesize heme derivatives and chlorophyll, the concentration of the latter being about a hundred times greater than that of the hemes. This implies regulatory mechanisms that maintain the flow of the common precursor, pro-

84

Table 5–1 Accumulation of porphyrins and precursors under normal and abnormal conditions[a]

Organism	Major tetrapyrrole derivative	Rate of synthesis	Porphyrins and precursors		
Man	Hemoglobin, 900 g ≡ 53 mmoles heme/ 70 kg body wt.	460 μmoles/day	Urinary excretion, μmoles/day	Normal {	Copro. 0.15
					Uro. 0.03
					ALA 20
					PBG <4
				Acute porphyria {	ALA 260–410
					PBG 310–440
R. spheroides	Bacteriochlorophyll, 25 μmoles/g dry wt.	10 μmoles/hr/ g dry wt.	Porphyrin in medium, μmoles/g of cells	Normal	~0.1
				Fe deficient	80

[a] The values quoted for man have been calculated from data provided by Drabkin (1951) and Mauzerall and Granick (1956).

85

Table 5–2 Effect of environment on the level of tetrapyrrole derivatives in various organisms

Organism	Environmental conditions	Tetrapyrrole derivative	Concentration	References[a]
Man	Low altitude	Hemoglobin, g/100 ml blood	16	(1)
	High altitude		23	
Daphnia pulex	High aeration	Hemoglobin, arbitrary units	19	(2)
	Low aeration		56	
Micrococcus denitrificans	High aeration	Cytochrome c, μm-moles/mg dry wt.	0.02	(3)
	Low aeration		0.05	
Chlorella pyrenoidosa	High light intensity	Chlorophyll $a + b$, μm-moles/mg dry wt.	30	(4)
	Low light intensity		54	
R. spheroides	High light intensity, anaerobic	Bacteriochlorophyll, μm-moles/mg dry wt.	7	(5)
	Low light intensity, anaerobic		56	
	Dark; high aeration		0.2	

[a] References: (1) Wintrobe, 1961; (2) Fox, 1947; (3) Chang, 1963; (4) Rabinowitch, 1945; (5) Cohen-Bazire, Sistrom, and Stanier, 1957.

toporphyrin, toward the different end products at the appropriate rate. The iron and magnesium branches of the biosynthetic pathway are apparently controlled independently, since chlorophyll synthesis can be repressed under certain circumstances without affecting heme synthesis.

Synthesis of the functional tetrapyrrole derivatives by animals, plants, and microorganisms is significantly influenced by the environment. The examples given in Table 5–2 show that organisms have the capacity to raise or repress tetrapyrrole synthesis according to the demands of the environment. Thus, hemoglobin synthesis in vertebrates is increased at high altitudes where the oxygen tension is low, while the water flea, *Daphnia,* makes considerably more of this pigment when grown in poorly aerated pond water. Many bacteria are richer in cytochromes when grown with limited aeration. In plants and photosynthetic bacteria chlorophyll synthesis is influenced by the light intensity, being maximal under a low intensity.

5–2   CONTROL OF METABOLIC PATHWAYS BY NEGATIVE FEEDBACK INHIBITION AND ENZYME REPRESSION

Before dealing in more detail with possible mechanisms by which tetrapyrrole synthesis is regulated, some consideration should be given to known regulatory mechanisms in the biosynthesis of essential metabolites such as amino acids and nucleic acid derivatives. The gearing of biosynthesis to avoid overproduction of intermediates and wasteful synthesis of unnecessary enzymes has been studied mostly in bacteria (Moyed and Umbarger, 1962). Two mechanisms have been firmly established: (1) feedback control of enzyme *action* and (2) feedback control of enzyme *formation* (repression). These mechanisms are presented in Scheme 5–1, where A, B, and C represent intermediates in the synthesis of the metabolite X.

In the known examples of control by inhibition of enzyme activity the end product inhibits the enzyme catalyzing the first step leading specifically to the end product. In repression the end product acts as a repressor of enzyme formation and in many instances synthesis of all the enzymes of the pathway is prevented (coordinate repression). Repressibility is under genetic control, since mutants have been isolated in which enzyme synthesis is no longer repressed by the end product.

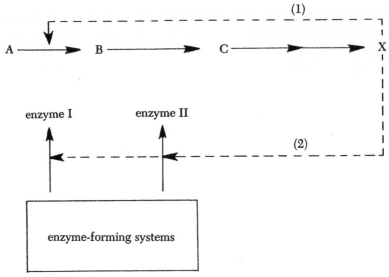

Scheme 5–1   Control by feedback inhibition (1) and repression (2).

The mechanism of feedback inhibition of enzyme action is quick to act and exerts a fine control on the flow of intermediates toward the end product. Repression takes longer to become effective in limiting the flow of intermediates, since the enzymes present in the cells before the onset of repression may continue to function until diluted out as the cells multiply. Repression is, however, important for the general economy of the cell since it prevents wasteful synthesis of enzyme proteins.

5–3   CONTROL OF TETRAPYRROLE SYNTHESIS IN MICROORGANISMS BY FEEDBACK INHIBITION AND REPRESSION

Although it is clear that higher organisms have regulatory mechanisms for controlling the supply of intermediates for tetrapyrrole synthesis and for adjusting the synthesis in response to the environment, control mechanisms have been studied mostly in bacteria. The high rate of synthesis achieved by microorganisms and the fact that they grow in defined media in environments that can be varied experimentally have undoubtedly been major reasons for this exploitation.

Photosynthetic bacteria in particular have been used. These organisms have the highest capacity among bacteria for tetrapyrrole synthesis, since they form both chlorophylls and hemes. The concentration of the former pigment is about one hundred times that of the latter, so that the main function of the tetrapyrrole-forming machinery is clearly to form chlorophyll. The photosynthetic bacteria must in addition have mechanisms that regulate the iron and magnesium branch of the pathway.

Negative Feedback Inhibition of Enzyme Action. Evidence that tetrapyrrole synthesis in bacteria is controlled by negative feedback inhibition of enzymes of the pathway is suggested by the accumulation of porphyrins occurring in iron deficiency (Table 2–6). This phenomenon has been studied in detail with suspensions of R. spheroides (Lascelles, 1956a). When iron-deficient suspensions are incubated anaerobically in the light with glycine and α-ketoglutarate, coproporphyrin III is excreted into the medium and attains concentrations up to 200 μm-moles/ml; there is only a small in-

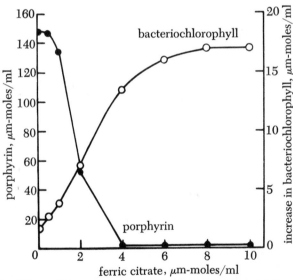

Figure 5–1   Effect of iron on porphyrin and bacteriochlorophyll formation by suspensions of R. spheroides. Iron-deficient suspensions were incubated in the light with glycine and α-ketoglutarate with added iron citrate as shown (from Lascelles, 1956a).

crease in bacteriochlorophyll in the cells. Upon addition of iron salts only traces of porphyrin are formed but bacteriochlorophyll is increased by about eightfold (Figure 5–1). The amount of porphyrins formed without iron is about one hundred times greater than the amount of total tetrapyrroles (bacteriochlorophyll and hemes) formed with iron. The excreted porphyrins therefore represent overproduction of an intermediate, as a result of the breakdown of a control mechanism.

Iron acts catalytically in preventing porphyrin accumulation by *R. spheroides;* thus, about 100 μm-moles of coproporphyrin fail to appear upon addition of only 2 μm-moles of iron citrate (Figure 5–1). This catalytic effect of iron suggests that it is needed to form a compound that controls an early step in tetrapyrrole synthesis by negative feedback inhibition. Evidence that this compound may be heme and that the inhibited enzyme is ALA synthetase has come from studies with whole cells and partially purified preparations of the synthetase (Burnham and Lascelles, 1963). Porphyrin accumulation by intact cells is inhibited by hemin when glycine and α-ketoglutarate are the substrates but no inhibition occurs with ALA as substrate (Table 5–3). The isolated enzyme is extremely sensitive to hemin, being inhibited significantly by concentrations as low as 0.1 μM (Table 5–4). The inhibition is noncompetitive with any of the substrates or cofactors of the syn-

Table 5–3   Effect of hemin on porphyrin synthesis by suspensions of *R. spheroides*[a]

Hemin, μM	Porphyrin, μm-moles/ml from	
	Glycine + α-ketoglutarate	ALA
Nil	31	31
5	16	
20	6	33

[a] Iron-deficient cells were incubated for 8 hours in the light with 10 mM glycine and α-ketoglutarate or with 2 mM ALA (Burnham and Lascelles, 1963).

Table 5–4   Effect of tetrapyrroles on ALA synthetase from *R. spheroides*[a]

Tetrapyrrole, μM	ALA formed, μmoles/hr/mg protein
Nil	1.70
Hemin 0.1	1.05
Hemin 1.0	0.89
Hemin 10	0.76
Heme 100	0.30
Iron deuteroporphyrin 25	0.71
Iron hematoporphyrin 25	0.78
Protoporphyrin 25	1.28
Hemoglobin 32	1.18
Myoglobin 2.7	1.11

[a] Partially purified enzyme was assayed for ALA synthetase in the presence of the tetrapyrroles as shown (Burnham and Lascelles, 1963). The concentration of hemoglobin and myoglobin is given as heme equivalents.

thetase but it is reversed by dilution. Although hemin is the most active inhibitor of those tested, other tetrapyrroles including hemato- and deuteroheme are also effective. It is significant that hemoglobin and myoglobin also inhibit the synthetase, since under normal conditions hemes within the cells are mostly if not entirely present as hemoproteins.

The results therefore suggest that one mechanism for the control of tetrapyrrole synthesis in *R. spheroides* is through negative feedback inhibition of ALA synthetase by heme, the formation of which is governed by the iron concentration (Scheme 5–2). Inhibition of ALA synthetase by hemin has so far been established only with the *R. spheroides* enzyme; clearly, it is important to examine other sources of the enzyme.

Feedback inhibition of ALA synthetase by heme does not satisfactorily account for all the effects of iron deficiency on porphyrin formation by bacteria. It is always coproporphyrin that accumulates; if iron were acting solely via heme, protoporphyrin might be expected. An additional site of action of iron is therefore indicated, viz., in the conversion of coproporphyrinogen to protoporphyrin; this possibility has been discussed in Section 3–1.

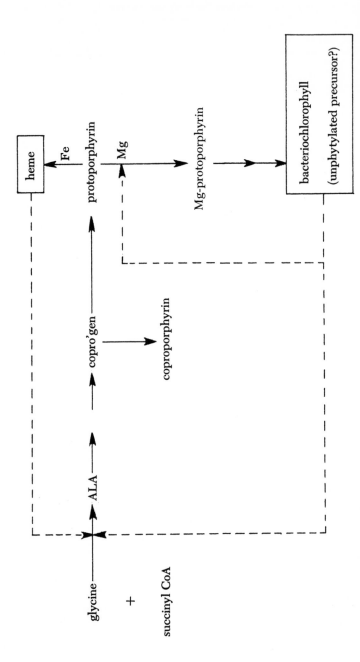

Scheme 5–2   Regulation of bacteriochlorophyll and heme synthesis in photosynthetic bacteria by negative feedback inhibition (largely hypothetical).

Control of the iron and magnesium branches of the pathway. Although *R. spheroides* is rich in hemoproteins the main function of ALA synthetase is for synthesis of ALA directed toward the formation of bacteriochlorophyll. It might therefore be expected that this pigment would inhibit the enzyme, but this could not be demonstrated with the isolated enzyme. This negative observation may have no physiological relevance, since bacteriochlorophyll is water-insoluble and probably does not exist as the free molecule in the cell. The possibility that bacteriochlorophyll or a precursor may act as a feedback inhibitor of the synthetase is supported by the observation that inhibition of bacteriochlorophyll formation by ethionine leads to the accumulation of porphyrins in *R. spheroides;* the analogue (as S-adenosylethionine) interferes with the methylation of magnesium protoporphyrin (Gibson et al., 1962). The fact that coproporphyrin, rather than protoporphyrin or its magnesium complex, accumulates under these conditions remains, however, to be explained.

By analogy with other branched biosynthetic pathways, which include a common intermediate leading to two or more end products, a negative feedback control might be predicted to act on the enzyme catalyzing the insertion of magnesium into protoporphyrin; the inhibitor might be the appropriate chlorophyll or possibly a nonphytylated precursor. This could lead to the diversion of protoporphyrin toward heme, which would in turn regulate the supply of intermediates for protoporphyrin synthesis by negative feedback inhibition of ALA synthetase (Scheme 5–2).

Enzyme Repression by Metabolites. Formation of ALA synthetase by growing cultures of *R. spheroides* is repressed by the addition of low concentrations (0.01 mM) of hemin (Lascelles, 1960). Other porphyrins and metal complexes do not affect enzyme synthesis. ALA dehydratase is also repressed by hemin suggesting that coordinate repression occurs as in other biosynthetic pathways subject to control by repression.

The action of hemin in repressing enzyme formation and inhibiting enzyme action is thus in accord with other biosyntheses that are regulated both by end product feedback inhibition and by repression. The repression by hemin poses the same problem, discussed above, of the significance of this effect as a regulatory mechanism in an organism forming bacteriochlorophyll as the predominant tetrapyrrole.

ALA is a potent repressor of ALA synthetase and ALA dehydratase in *R. spheroides* (Lascelles, 1960). The physiological significance of this observation is difficult to assess. The true repressor may be a metabolite formed from ALA; cultures growing in the presence of ALA accumulate chlorophyll derivatives that have yet to be identified.

5–4   PHYSIOLOGICAL ADAPTATION OF MICROORGANISMS TO THEIR ENVIRONMENT

Effect of Oxygen on Hemoprotein Formation. The concentration of hemoproteins in microorganisms shows considerable variation according to the oxygen pressure of the environment (Tables 5–5 and 5–6). Two types of response have been observed with different organisms.

1. In certain facultative anaerobes hemoproteins are formed maximally only in the presence of oxygen, i.e., oxygen exerts an inducing effect on hemoprotein synthesis (Table 5–5).

2. In many bacteria the cytochrome content is increased as the oxygen pressure is decreased, i.e., oxygen exerts a repressing effect on the synthesis (Table 5–6).

Induction by oxygen. The inducing effect of oxygen has been studied in detail with yeast, particularly by Slonimski (1953, 1956). In anaerobically grown *Saccharomyces cerevisiae* only cytochromes a_1 and b are detectable spectroscopically, but upon aeration of the cells in buffered glucose cytochromes, *a, a_3, b,* and *c,* typical of aerobically grown cells, develop rapidly. The changes in

Table 5–5   Inducing effect of oxygen on hemoprotein synthesis

Organism	Hemoprotein	Concentration		References[a]
		Aerobic	Anaerobic	
S. cerevisiae	Cytochrome $a + a_3$	14	0	(1)
	Cytochrome b	12	1.5	
	Cytochrome c, μm-moles/g wet wt.	16	2	
B. cereus	Cytochrome c, μm-moles/mg N	0.64	Not detectable	(2)
R. spheroides	Catalase, mg per cent dry wt.	150	2	(3)

[a] References: (1) Barrett (1962); (2) Schaeffer (1952); (3) Clayton (1960).

Table 5–6   Repressing effect of oxygen on cytochrome c synthesis

Organism	Growth conditions, % O_2		Cytochrome c, μm-moles/mg protein	References[a]
Ps. fluorescens	Aerobic	1	3.3	(1)
		5	2.0	
		10	1.0	
		20	0.25	
		50	0.17	
Micrococcus	Aerobic—high aeration		0.04	(2)
denitrificans	Aerobic—low aeration		0.10	
	Anaerobic with nitrate		0.21	

[a] References: (1) Lenhoff, Nicholas and Kaplan (1956); (2) Chang (1963).

cytochromes are accompanied by a rise in respiration, hence the term *adaptation respiratoire*. A similar phenomenon occurs upon aeration of anaerobically grown *Pasteurella pestis* (Engelsberg, Levy, and Gibor, 1954); the cells are initially devoid of cytochromes but form cytochrome *b* and free hematin when aerated. In *Bacillus cereus* cytochromes *a, b,* and *c* are found in cells grown aerobically, whereas only cytochrome *b* is detectable in those grown anaerobically and the total heme content is one-fifth of that in the aerobic organisms (Schaeffer, 1952).

Besides cytochromes other hemoproteins are induced by oxygen. In yeast cytochrome peroxidase and catalase are developed by aeration (Chantrenne, 1954). The catalase content of *R. spheroides* is about one hundred times higher in aerobic organisms than in those grown anaerobically in the light, and the enzyme is induced by aeration of suspensions of cells grown under the latter conditions (Clayton, 1960).

In the instances where oxygen-induced hemoprotein synthesis has been studied in cell suspensions the phenomenon is obligatorily linked to protein synthesis, since it is inhibited by *p*-fluorophenylalanine and other analogues that prevent the formation of protein and nucleic acid. Direct evidence that oxygen induces the synthesis of both the protein and prosthetic group components of the hemoproteins has been shown by the incorporation of C^{14}-glycine into each moiety of cytochrome *c* during adaptation of yeast suspensions (Yčas and Drabkin, 1957). Oxygen is, therefore, not acting solely by permitting the synthesis of the heme prosthetic group; the primary effect could be in inducing the formation of specific proteins. Besides the hemoproteins, enzymes of the tricarboxylic acid cycle are induced by oxygen in yeast and *P. pestis*. In the case of yeast there are also changes in internal structure suggesting that the mitochondria are formed in response to oxygen (Linnane, Vitols, and Nowland, 1962; Schatz, Tuppy, and Klima, 1963). Since the operation of the tricarboxylic acid cycle is necessary to provide succinyl CoA for tetrapyrrole synthesis, the action of oxygen in permitting the formation of the prosthetic group of the hemoproteins may be due ultimately to its effect on the formation of enzymes of the cycle. The mechanism by which oxygen induces these complex changes in the enzyme makeup and structure of cells is unknown.

Repression by oxygen. The apparent antithesis of induction of hemoprotein synthesis by oxygen is found in many bacteria in which the concentration of cytochromes varies inversely with the oxygen pressure. This is clearly seen in *Pseudomonas fluorescens* (Table 5–6); the cytochrome *c* content varies over a twentyfold range when grown in atmospheres between 1 and 50 per cent oxygen. Striking changes in cytochrome content are exhibited by denitrifying bacteria that can grow anaerobically with nitrate as terminal oxidant (Verhoeven and Takeda, 1956). Under the latter conditions the level of cytochromes *b* and *c* in *Micrococcus denitrificans* is about five times higher than in cells grown with high aeration (Chang, 1963). This is due to repression of cytochrome synthesis by oxygen rather than to induction by nitrate, since cytochrome formation is enhanced in a nitrate-free medium provided the oxygen concentration is reduced (Table 5–6). Cytochrome *c* synthesis by *Escherichia coli* is also repressed by oxygen, the level in anaerobically grown cells being ten times higher than in aerobically grown organisms (Wimpenny, Ranlett, and Gray, 1963). Upon transfer of anaerobic cultures to aerobic conditions, the cytochrome *c* concentration falls rapidly, suggesting preferential turnover of the hemoprotein.

The concentration of oxygen markedly influences the level of *a*-type cytochromes in those organisms which contain these components of the electron transport chain. In *Aerobacter aerogenes* cytochrome a_2 increases as the oxygen concentration is lowered to $1 \mu M$ (Moss, 1956); at concentrations less than this the level of the cytochrome falls. Similar observations have been made with *Hemophilus parainfluenzae* (White, 1962).

As in the case of oxygen induction, nothing is known of the

mechanism of oxygen repression of hemoprotein synthesis. It is likely that formation of both the protein and prosthetic group components is influenced by oxygen. Thus, synthesis of cytochromes *b* and *c* by suspensions of *M. denitrificans* under low aeration depends on a source of cell nitrogen and is inhibited by analogues that prevent protein synthesis (Chang, 1963). The elaboration of enzymes for tetrapyrrole synthesis could also account for the requirement for protein synthesis. There is however no evidence which supports either possibility.

Environmental Factors in Chlorophyll Synthesis. Studies of the effect of environment on the synthesis of chlorophyll by plants and photosynthetic bacteria have distinct advantages from the experimental point of view; the concentration of these pigments varies considerably under appropriate conditions and unlike most hemoproteins they are readily estimated.

Effect of oxygen on bacteriochlorophyll formation: repression of ALA synthetase. Photosynthetic bacteria of the Athiorhodaceae group (e.g., *R. spheroides*) exhibit an impressive response to the environment. They are deeply pigmented when grown anaerobically in the light but contain only traces of pigment when grown in the dark with high aeration. Variations in the photosynthetic pigments, bacteriochlorophyll, and carotenoids, are responsible for these changes.

The work of Cohen-Bazire, Sistrom, and Stanier (1957) established that bacteriochlorophyll synthesis by *R. spheroides* is repressed by oxygen even in the presence of light. Pigment synthesis by cultures growing anaerobically under continuous illumination ceases immediately upon introduction of oxygen (Figure 5–2). The importance of oxygen as a repressing agent is shown by the fact that bacteriochlorophyll synthesis occurs *in the dark* under low oxygen pressure (Table 5–7). There is an inverse relation be-

Table 5–7   Concentration of bacteriochlorophyll and ALA synthetase in *R. spheroides*

Growth conditions, % O_2	Bacteriochlorophyll, μm-moles/mg dry wt cells	ALA synthetase, units/mg protein
Aerobic–dark, 6	22	340
20	0.2	56
Anaerobic–light	24	320

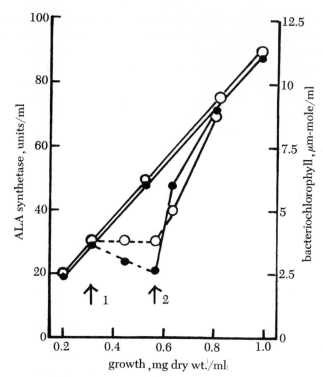

Figure 5–2   Repression by oxygen of ALA synthetase and dehydratase in growing cultures of *R. spheroides*. The culture was grown anaerobically until the point marked by the arrow (1) when it was divided. One portion received further incubation aerobically broken lines) until the point marked by arrow (2), when anaerobic conditions were restored. The control (full lines) was incubated anaerobically throughout the experimental period. All cultures were incubated with continuous illumination. • = enzyme; ○ = bacteriochlorophyll (from Lascelles, 1960).

tween the amount of pigment formed and the oxygen concentration, and the phenomenon therefore bears a striking resemblance to the response of nonphotosynthetic bacteria with respect to cytochrome synthesis (Table 5–6).

There is now considerable evidence that the level of ALA synthetase has an important role in the regulation of bacteriochlorophyll formation. The concentration of this enzyme in *R. spheroides* grown under various conditions is correlated with the capacity to form bacteriochlorophyll (Table 5–7). It is high in cells grown anaerobically in the light or in the dark under reduced aeration, i.e., under conditions that promote pigment synthesis. In nonpigmented cells, grown under high aeration, the enzyme level is only one-fifth to one-tenth that in the pigmented organisms.

Repression of ALA synthetase by oxygen is shown by experiments with cultures of R. *spheroides* (Lascelles, 1960). When growing under high aeration the enzyme is formed at one-third or less the rate in cultures growing anaerobically in the light. Introduction of oxygen into cultures growing under the latter conditions (and therefore forming enzyme and pigment at a high rate) results in the immediate repression of synthetase formation (Figure 5–2). This effect of oxygen is readily reversed; upon restoration of anaerobic conditions, formation of ALA synthetase and of bacteriochlorophyll resumes at a high rate (Figure 5–2).

Synthesis of the enzyme has also been studied with cell suspensions of R. *spheroides* adapting from the nonpigmented (high aeration) to the pigmented state (low aeration) (Lascelles, 1959; Bull and Lascelles, 1963). Upon incubation under low oxygen pressure, there is an immediate rise in ALA synthetase, which precedes bacteriochlorophyll synthesis (Figure 5–3). The increase in enzyme activity under these conditions presumably involves de novo protein synthesis rather than the unmasking of preformed enzyme, since it is inhibited by chloramphenicol and other protein synthesis inhibitors and is dependent on a source of cell nitrogen.

These studies with R. *spheroides* have shown that ALA synthetase behaves as expected of a repressible enzyme; upon removal of the repressor, in this case oxygen acting either directly or indirectly, enzyme synthesis occurs immediately. The synthetase is never completely repressed even in cells grown under high aeration, and under these conditions is required for the synthesis of the prosthetic groups of the hemoproteins. This raises the question of whether the photosynthetic bacteria have two distinct ALA synthetases, one for bacteriochlorophyll synthesis, subject to oxygen repression, and the other for heme formation. Although there is no evidence in this particular case, there are known precedents for different enzymes catalyzing the same reaction, under independent control, in other biosynthetic pathways that involve a common intermediate (Stadtman, 1963).

Rapid destruction of the enzyme may be another mechanism for adjusting the rate of bacteriochlorophyll synthesis to suit the environment. In R. *spheroides* the synthetase is apparently subject

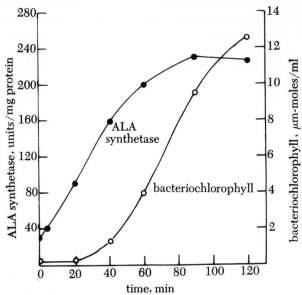

Figure 5–3   Formation of ALA synthetase and bacteriochlorophyll under low aeration by suspensions of *R. spheroides*. Cells grown with high aeration were incubated in fresh growth medium under low aeration (from Lascelles, 1959).

to rapid turnover. Enzyme activity declines when cells containing a high level of the synthetase are transferred to (1) conditions in which protein synthesis is blocked (Bull and Lascelles, 1963) or (2) conditions of high aeration (see Figure 5–2).

Repression of ALA synthetase is certainly not the complete answer to the problem of how oxygen prevents bacteriochlorophyll formation. This is shown by the immediate and complete cessation of pigment synthesis upon the introduction of oxygen into cultures growing anaerobically in the light (Figure 5–2). If enzyme repression were the only factor involved, pigment synthesis should proceed but at a constantly diminishing rate as preformed ALA synthetase becomes diluted out by continued growth of the cells. The immediate stoppage suggests that oxygen has additional effects, leading to direct inhibition of the action of enzymes of the biosynthetic pathway. Such effects have not been demonstrated with enzymes from *R. spheroides*. In preparations from chick erythrocytes, however, oxygen has been shown to inhibit (although not completely) the conversion of PBG to uroporphyrinogen (Falk and Porra, 1963).

Oxygen repression of other enzymes involved in bacteriochlorophyll synthesis. There is every indication that coordinate repression by oxygen occurs with enzymes of the bacteriochlorophyll pathway in *R. spheroides*. The level of ALA dehydratase shows the same variations as the synthetase in response to the oxygen pressure (Lascelles, 1959; 1960). Enzymes catalyzing the conversion of PBG to uro- and coproporphyrinogen are also apparently repressed by oxygen, since the over-all conversion occurs at a higher rate in extracts of pigmented cells than in those from aerobically grown (nonpigmented) organisms. The enzyme catalyzing the methylation of magnesium protoporphyrin is not detectable in preparations from the latter type of cells, suggesting that oxygen repression may extend along the entire biosynthetic pathway (Gibson et al., 1963).

Effect of light. The bacteriochlorophyll concentration in photosynthetic bacteria (under anaerobic conditions) varies inversely with the light intensity (Cohen-Bazire et al., 1957; Table 5–2). As with oxygen, high light intensity represses ALA synthetase (Lascelles, 1960). The effects of light intensity and oxygen thus bear a close resemblance and suggest that the ultimate controlling mechanism is the same in each case. Cohen-Bazire et al. (1957), have postulated that pigment synthesis is regulated by the concentration of a carrier in the electron transport chain; the redox state of a component of the chain may have to attain a certain critical level before pigment synthesis can ensue. Both oxygen and light cause the oxidation of reduced cytochromes and other electron carriers in whole cells and chromatophores of photosynthetic bacteria (Nishimura and Chance, 1963). There is, however, no direct evidence for a correlation between the steady-state concentration of electron transport carriers and the ability to form pigments.

5–5 CONTROL OF CHLOROPHYLL SYNTHESIS IN PLANTS

The same problems exist for plants as for photosynthetic bacteria with respect to the regulation of the iron and magnesium branch of tetrapyrrole synthesis. How plants solve these problems is even less clear. As with the bacteria, chlorophyll synthesis by algae and higher plants is influenced by the light intensity. In *Chlorella,* for instance, the concentration of chlorophyll is highest in cells grown with low illumination (Table 5–2), while in higher plants the shade leaves are richer in pigment than those exposed to the sun (Rabinowitch, 1945).

The light-dependence of the later stages of chlorophyll synthesis and of chloroplast development in higher plants and some algae has been already discussed. There is clear evidence that the greening process is regulated in some way, since the concentration of MgVP (in protein-bound form) in etiolated leaves is only about one-tenth of the chlorophyll ultimately formed after exposure to light. Illumination, therefore, may release a control that prevents the action of enzymes leading to MgVP formation. Free MgVP is not the controlling factor, since etiolated leaves that have been allowed to accumulate free MgVP by exposure to ALA in the dark form chlorophyll at the normal rate upon illumination from endogenous precursors (Granick, 1963a). The possibility remains that the protein-bound form of MgVP, presumed to be the true intermediate, exerts some form of control on the action of the enzymes leading to its synthesis.

Repression may also operate on enzymes of chlorophyll synthesis and this may be released on exposure to light. There is no information about the level of the biosynthetic enzymes in etiolated and green plants except for the observation that chlorophyllase increases rapidly upon transfer of etiolated seedlings to the light (Holden, 1961).

5–6 CONTROL MECHANISMS IN HEME SYNTHESIS BY ANIMAL TISSUES

Little is known about how tetrapyrrole synthesis is regulated in animal tissues. It may be misleading to extrapolate extensively from observations with unicellular microorganisms to multicellular higher animals. Nevertheless the synthesis of tetrapyrrole derivatives must be ultimately regulated in all tissues at the level of the enzyme-catalyzed steps in the biosynthetic pathway.

Tissue Specialization. The localization of hemoglobin synthesis in specialized erythropoietic tissues in higher animals has overcome one problem, the simultaneous manufacture of massive amounts of hemoglobin and the very minor amounts of other equally essential hemoproteins such as cytochromes.

Table 5–8   Activity of enzymes of heme biosynthesis in rabbit tissue

	Activity	
Tissue	ALA dehydratase[a]	Coproporphyrinogen oxidase[b]
Liver	1.05	0.144
Bone marrow	0.24	0.09
Kidney	0.25	0.041
Brain	0.06	0.035
Heart muscle	0.04	0.012
Small intestine	0.04	0.002

[a] μmoles PBG/hr/g fresh wt (Gibson et al., 1955).
[b] μmoles protoporphyrin/hr/g fresh wt (Sano and Granick, 1961).

The hemoprotein levels in tissues vary considerably. Besides differences in the levels of cytochromes according to the metabolic activity (Drabkin, 1951), some tissues also contain large quantities of other hemoproteins, e.g., catalase and myoglobin. There is clear evidence that the cells of various tissues synthesize their own set of hemoproteins de novo (Marsh and Drabkin, 1957). Cells of a given tissue must therefore have mechanisms for keeping in step the synthesis of the specific proteins and tetrapyrrole moieties to maintain the characteristic ratios of the various hemoproteins.

Although information is far from complete, there does seem to be a correlation between the distribution and level of enzymes on the biosynthetic pathway and the capacity of tissues to form hemoproteins (Table 5–8; see Chapter 3). Thus enzyme activity is high in liver and bone marrow but low in the small intestine. These observations suggest that the concentration of the biosynthetic enzymes determines, at least partly, the amount of tetrapyrrole formed by a tissue, but crucial information about the activity of ALA synthetase in different organs is lacking.

Compartmentation of Biosynthetic Enzymes. The intracellular distribution of enzymes on the biosynthetic pathway to heme may play an important part in regulation of the synthesis (Sano and Granick, 1961). The enzymes catalyzing the conversion of ALA to coproporphyrinogen are in the soluble fraction of animal cells whereas ALA synthetase and the enzymes converting coproporphyrinogen

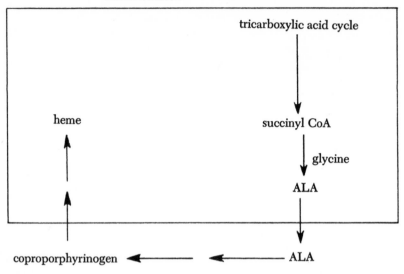

Scheme 5–3   Distribution of enzymes of heme biosynthesis (after Sano and Granick, 1961).

to heme are mitochondrial. ALA must therefore be released from the mitochondria before becoming available for tetrapyrrole synthesis (Scheme 5–3). Thus, the synthesis may be regulated by the rate of leakage of ALA from and of coproporphyrinogen back into the mitochondria; this could involve specific permeases, although there is no evidence for this (Granick, 1962). The steady-state concentration of ALA within mitochondria could be important in determining the egress of ALA and this could in turn be governed by the level of succinyl CoA generated by the tricarboxylic acid cycle.

Effect of Oxygen. It is striking that the synthesis of tetrapyrrole derivatives is influenced by the oxygen pressure in animals as well as in microorganisms. This is seen in invertebrates such as *Daphnia* where the hemoglobin concentration is inversely proportional to the oxygen concentration (Fox, 1955). In higher animals erythropoiesis is regulated by the oxygen tension of the arterial blood. Anoxia, caused by reducing the atmospheric pressure or by diseases affecting pulmonary ventilation or the circulatory system, results in polycythemia (Wintrobe, 1961). Conversely, red cell formation is depressed by inspiration of high tensions of oxygen. The response to oxygen of the erythriopoietic systems of higher animals is complex and certainly cannot be interpreted solely in terms of effects on enzymes of tetrapyrrole synthesis. An important factor may be erythiopoietin, a hormone-like substance in serum, which stimulates red cell formation; its level may be controlled by the oxygen pressure (Gordon, 1959; Wintrobe, 1961). The recent observation that erythropoietin stimulates heme synthesis in vitro (in cultures of bone marrow cells) offers possibilities of more precise studies of its mode of action (Kranz, Gallien-Lartigue, and Goldwasser, 1963).

In vitro studies have shown effects of oxygen on various steps in the biosynthetic pathway to heme. The obligatory requirement for oxygen as oxidant in the conversion of coproporphyrinogen to protoporphyrin by animal tissues has already been discussed. Oxygen also inhibits some of the steps, for instance, heme synthetase (Porra and Jones, 1963). Also the formation of protoporphyrin from glycine by avian hemolysates occurs optimally at oxygen pressures less than atmospheric; above and below 7 per cent oxygen, protoporphyrin synthesis is decreased (Falk, Porra, Brown, Moss, and Larminie, 1959). The oxygen-sensitive step is in the conversion of PBG to uroporphyrinogen (Falk and Porra, 1963). This inhibition is reversible and the effect could therefore be a mechanism for controlling tetrapyrrole synthesis according to the prevailing oxygen pressure. Whether this inhibition is significant for changes of oxygen pressure to be expected in erythiopoietic tissues is open to question.

Most of the enzymes of the biosynthetic pathway (including ALA synthetase and dehydratase) require SH groups for activity. Oxygen could influence enzyme activity by altering the availability of SH groups.

5–7   ROLE OF TRICARBOXYLIC ACID CYCLE

ALA synthetase in various tissues is in competition with several enzymes for which succinyl CoA is a substrate. How does the synthetase obtain enough of the thioester to maintain the level of tetrapyrrole derivatives? The relative concentration of the competing enzymes and their affinity for the substrate must be highly important in this situation; the rise and fall of the synthetase in parallel with the rate of tetrapyrrole synthesis in R. *spheroides* has already been discussed.

The intracellular concentration of succinyl CoA or succinate may also be important in regulating the synthesis. The key role of the tricarboxylic acid cycle in providing succinyl CoA has been mentioned in Chapter 3, and the rate at which this cycle operates could therefore influence tetrapyrrole formation. It is in this region of the cycle that oxygen might also affect the synthesis.

Formation and utilization of succinyl CoA. In the normally operating cycle succinyl CoA is converted to succinate by succinic thiokinase (succinyl CoA synthetase; Hager, 1962), which catalyzes the re-action:

$$\text{succinyl CoA} + \text{nucleotidediphosphate} + Pi \rightleftharpoons$$
$$\text{succinate} + \text{CoA} + \text{nucleotidetriphosphate}$$

The succinate is then rapidly removed by oxidation. Since succinic thiokinase is reversible, succinyl CoA can be formed either by oxidation of α-ketoglutarate or directly from succinate (Scheme 5–4); there is now ample evidence that the thioester can come from both sources in heme synthesis by animal tissues. This is summarized as follows:

1. Incorporation of methylene-labeled succinate into heme by duck erythrocytes is considerably decreased by malonate, but incorporation of carboxyl-labeled succinate is not inhibited (Shemin and Kumin, 1952; see Scheme 3–2). The carboxyl-labeled compound loses its label when oxidized via the cycle and could therefore be incorporated into heme only by direct conversion to succinyl CoA.

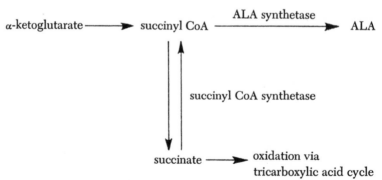

Scheme 5–4   Succinyl CoA in the tricarboxylic acid cycle.

2. Seconal, which inhibits oxidation of $NADH_2$, also prevents the incorporation into heme of methylene but not carboxyl-labeled succinate by rat liver homogenates (Onisawa and Labbe, 1963). Since the formation of succinyl CoA from the methylene-labeled compound via the cycle involves two NAD-linked steps, inhibition of $NADH_2$ oxidation would therefore decrease succinate incorporation into heme; this is confirmed by the reversal of seconal inhibition by acetoacetate, which acts as an acceptor for $NADH_2$ oxidation.

3. The two sources of succinyl CoA have been demonstrated directly by Granick and Urata (1963) with liver mitochondria from DDC-poisoned guinea pigs (see Section 5–8). Arsenite (which inhibits the oxidative decarboxylation of α-ketoglutarate) strongly inhibits ALA formation from glycine plus α-ketoglutarate, isocitrate, or citrate, but its effect with succinate as substrate is less marked. With the former substrates, 85 per cent of the succinyl CoA comes from α-ketoglutarate while with succinate as substrate 60 per cent of the succinyl CoA comes directly without traveling through the cycle.

The rate at which succinyl CoA is removed by the tricarboxylic acid cycle could have a considerable influence on tetrapyrrole synthesis, and any block in the conversion of succinyl CoA to succinate would favor its diversion to ALA. Direct evidence for this comes again from the DDC-mitochondrial system (Granick and Urata, 1963). Thus, ALA formation from α-ketoglutarate or citrate is inhibited by ADP and phosphate but enhanced by ATP; conversion of succinyl CoA to succinate by succinic thiokinase would be favored by ADP and phosphate, whereas ATP would favor succinyl CoA accumulation. Also, incubation of the mitochondria in nitrogen instead of air increases the yield of ALA; anaerobiosis would prevent oxidation of succinate and again favor succinyl CoA accumulation.

Effect of oxygen. Oxygen may exert an important controlling influence on tetrapyrrole synthesis by its effect on this area of the tricarboxylic acid cycle. Under semianaerobic conditions succinate oxidation is the limiting step in the cycle, since the redox potential of the succinate-fumarate system makes impossible major net hydrogen transfer from succinate to physiological acceptors other than oxygen (via catalysts of the electron transfer chain) (Krebs and Lowenstein, 1960). This is shown by the accumulation of succinate under anaerobic conditions by many microorganisms; yeast, for instance, accumulates more than 1 per cent of its dry weight as succinate anaerobically. Changes in the steady-state concentration of succinyl CoA, governed by the rate of succinate oxidation by the cycle, could be a delicate mechanism for regulating tetrapyrrole synthesis. Highly aerobic conditions would favor metabolism of succinyl CoA by the cycle but with limiting oxygen concentration more succinyl CoA may become available for diversion toward tetrapyrrole formation. Direct experimental support for this is provided by the observation that anaerobiosis increases the yield of ALA in the DDC-mitochondrial system (Granick and Urata, 1963).

5–8 EFFECT OF DRUGS

Experimental porphyria is induced in animals by administration of various drugs including Sedormid (allylisopropylacetyl urea), allylisopropylacetamide, and 3,5-dicarbethoxydihydro-collidine (DDC). The seat of the lesion is in the liver, which accumulates ALA, PBG, and porphyrins; these are also excreted in large amounts in the urine (Schmid and Schwarz, 1955; Granick and Mauzerall, 1961; Goldberg and Rimington, 1962). The large quantities of these substances indicate that the drugs interfere with the control of the biosynthetic pathway.

Recent work by Granick and Urata (1963) has shown that the ALA synthetase of liver plays a dominant part in the reaction to the drugs. The activity of this enzyme is low in mitochondria from normal guinea pig liver but in preparations from DDC-treated animals ALA synthetase is considerably increased. Thus, after incubation for 2 hours with glycine, α-ketoglutarate and cofactors, 25 to 45 μm-moles of ALA were formed per ml of packed normal mitochondria to be compared with 1000 to 2000 μm-moles by DDC-mitochondria. The activity of other enzymes of the biosynthetic pathway (ALA dehydratase and coproporphyrinogenase) did not differ significantly in livers from normal and treated animals, although Gibson et al. (1955) found a twofold increase in dehydratase activity of liver and kidney from Sedormid-treated animals. These important observations have been confirmed and extended by elegant experiments with chick embryo liver cells cultured on microscope slides (Granick, 1963c). Addition of allylisopropylacetamide or DDC to such slide cultures resulted in the accumulation of porphyrin (measured by fluorescence microscopy) within a few hours. Porphyrin formation depended on de novo protein synthesis, since it was inhibited by mitomycin, actinomycin, p-fluorophenylalanine and other compounds that block protein synthesis at various stages.

The conclusion from these studies is that drugs which cause acute porphyria induce the formation of ALA synthetase. Under normal circumstances ALA synthetase is apparently the rate-limiting step; other enzymes of the pathway are not limiting and an increase in the synthetase makes available more ALA for conversion to porphyrins by the other enzymes of the pathway. A crucial question still to be answered is how the porphyria-inducing drugs act on the ALA synthetase-forming system.

The enhanced formation of ALA synthetase does not account for all the effects of porphyria-inducing drugs on liver. In particular, Sedormid administration causes a rapid fall in liver catalase, but not in other hemoproteins, in rabbits, and rats (Schmid and Schwarz, 1955; Schmid, Figen, and Schwarz, 1955). This phenomenon is apparently connected with the increase in porphyrin formation, since they occur simultaneously. Incorporation of C^{14}-glycine into the catalase heme of Sedormid-treated animals is insignificant compared with normal animals, suggesting that the drug blocks the synthesis of the liver enzyme. If the sole effect of the drug on liver is to increase the level of ALA synthetase then either no change in the level of hemoproteins should occur (since other steps in the biosynthetic pathway may become limiting) or they should increase. In any case a change in the ratio of the various hemoproteins would not be expected. It is not known whether the block in catalase synthesis is due primarily to inhibition of the synthesis of the protein component or of the prosthetic group. The in vitro system developed by Granick offers possibilities for further analysis of this problem.

5–9 INTEGRATION OF PROTEIN SYNTHESIS
WITH TETRAPYRROLE FORMATION

In the discussion so far emphasis has been placed on the regulation of synthesis of the tetrapyrrole structure. Yet in nature the pigments are bound to specific proteins that are quite often associated with special cell organelles (mitochondria, chloroplasts, chromatophores). It is at least as important for the cell to have control over synthesis of the protein components as over that of the prosthetic groups, which comprise 5 per cent or less by weight of the hemoprotein molecules. One must presume that mechanisms exist for integrating the synthesis of the prosthetic group to match the supply of specific protein. That this is under genetic control is suggested by the isolation by Clayton and Smith (1960) of a mutant strain of *R. spheroides* which forms excessive amounts of catalase (5 to 25 per cent of its dry weight). Presumably a single alteration in the genome has resulted in the ability of the organism to form abnormal quantities of the specific protein, together with matching amounts of heme prosthetic group.

Hemoprotein Synthesis. In the case of hemoprotein synthesis in response to oxygen the available evidence indicates that the protein and prosthetic group are formed concurrently although not necessarily at the same rate. The isotope experiments of Yčas and Drabkin (1957) with yeast suggest that the protein moiety of cytochrome *c* is formed at a faster rate than the heme.

Synthesis of the protein component can also occur quite independently of the prosthetic group. Thus bone marrow suspensions continue to form globin when heme synthesis is blocked by cobalt ions (Morell, Savoie, and London, 1958) and a mutant strain of *Staphylococcus aureus*, unable to form heme, nevertheless forms the protein components of catalase and cytochromes when grown without heme (Jensen, 1957; Chang and Lascelles, 1963). There is less evidence to show whether formation of the heme moiety can proceed independently of the specific proteins. The formation of the prosthetic group may occur only when the specific protein is being formed, since inhibition of hemoprotein formation by blocking protein synthesis has not been reported to lead to an accumulation of hemes or precursors.

Clearly, much more information is needed about the integration of the two aspects of hemoprotein synthesis. The problem is open to attack by isotopic techniques; an experimental system is required in which a specific, easily isolated hemoprotein is formed in response to a stimulus such as oxygen. Besides the adapting yeast system, the high catalase mutant of *R. spheroides* offers considerable opportunities for further exploitation, since it forms such large amounts of catalase when exposed to oxygen.

Formation of hemoglobin by cell-free systems from reticulocytes is now being pursued by many workers investigating the mechanism of protein synthesis (Simpson, 1962). Since this protein is readily purified and recognized, these systems make possible the study of the formation of a specific protein. No attention appears to have been given to the synthesis of heme in this work. The in vitro systems may ultimately lead to an understanding of how the synthesis of hemoglobin is controlled.

Chlorophyll Synthesis. The association of the later stages of chlorophyll synthesis with protein synthesis by plants and photosynthetic bacteria has been described in Chapter 4. The situation is more complex than that of the formation of hemoproteins, since a specific protein component to which chlorophyll is attached has yet to be isolated.

In photosynthetic bacteria of the Athiorhodaceae family synthesis of bacteriochlorophyll by cells adapting from the nonpigmented to the pigmented state is accompanied by the preferential synthesis of chromatophore protein (Bull and Lascelles, 1963). This was shown by following the incorporation of labeled amino acids into the chromatophore and soluble protein fractions of the cells. Synthesis of the chromatophore protein is closely associated with pigment formation and responds to changes in the environment (e.g., oxygen concentration) in the same way. The nature of the newly formed chromatophore protein is not known. It could be the protein to which intermediates of bacteriochlorophyll synthesis are possibly bound; this could end up as structural protein (to which the completed pigment is attached) in the chromatophore. Another possibility is that the new proteins might largely consist of enzymes concerned in the synthesis of the pigment itself and/or enzymes of photosynthetic metabolism.

The simultaneous development with chlorophyll of the cell organelles, i.e., the chloroplasts of plants and the chromatophores of photosynthetic bacteria bears many similarities to the development of mitochondria in yeast adapting from anaerobic to aerobic conditions (Linnane, Vitols, and Nowland, 1962; Schatz, Tuppy, and Klima, 1963; Schatz, 1963). In each case the newly formed organelle bears not only the tetrapyrrole derivatives in a functional form but also other components of the electron transport chain as well as enzymes of the tricarboxylic acid cycle, in the case of yeast, and of photosynthetic metabolism in the case of plants and the bacteria.

The problem of how these changes are controlled requires an experimental attack with biochemical, cytological, and genetical techniques.

EPILOGUE

After this survey of the current state of knowledge of tetrapyrrole biosynthesis an assessment can now be made of the outstanding gaps and of possible areas of future development.

THE PATHWAY TO HEME

The established intermediates in the pathway to heme may be put into the following sequence:

$$
\begin{array}{c}
\text{glycine} \rightarrow \text{ALA} \rightarrow \text{PBG} ----\rightarrow \text{uroporphyrinogen} \\
\hspace{3cm} + \hspace{5cm} \text{III} \\
\hspace{1cm}\text{succinyl CoA} \hspace{4cm} \downarrow \\
\text{heme} \leftarrow \text{protoporphyrin} \leftarrow \text{protoporphyrinogen} \leftarrow -- \text{coproporphyrinogen} \\
\hspace{8cm} \text{III}
\end{array}
$$

The dashed arrows indicate the regions of mystery and speculation.

The intermediates between the monopyrrole PBG and the tetrapyrrole structure of uroporphyrinogen III are yet to be established. The decarboxylations necessary to transform uroporphyrinogen III (with eight carboxyl groups) to the next established intermediate, coproporphyrinogen III (four carboxyl groups) probably proceed stepwise since porphyrins with 7, 6, and 5 carboxyl groups have been detected by chromatography in various experimental systems, but the arrangement of these groups about the tetrapyrrole nucleus is unknown. There is a similar ignorance of the decarboxylation steps between coproporphyrinogen III and protoporphyrinogen; the over-all reaction also involves oxidation of the sidechains that finally appear as vinyl groups.

Further studies at an enzymic level are needed to fill in these gaps. Major problems to be faced by the experimenter in this field are the chemical instability of the intermediates and the difficulties of obtaining supplies of known intermediates. The only practical source of PBG, for instance, is the urine of porphyric animals.

Enzymes catalyzing the known steps have been obtained in varying degrees of purity, the greatest success being with ALA dehydratase from beef liver and heme synthetase from avian red cells. The achievement of purified enzymes should lead to information of the precise mechanism of the reactions catalyzed by them. The unique nature of many of the steps is a challenge to the enzymologist.

THE PATHWAY TO CHLOROPHYLL

The unknowns in the biosynthesis of chlorophyll from the magnesium protoporphyrin stage far exceed the known intermediates. Only two steps have been established, namely the methylation of magnesium protoporphyrin to the monomethyl ester and the light-dependent reduction of MgVP on the holochrome complex from higher plants to give chlorophyllide *a*.

The inability to obtain cell-free systems capable of converting magnesium protoporphyrin or the methyl ester to chlorophyll has been a major barrier to progress in elucidating the pathway. The later stages of chlorophyll synthesis and, possibly, the earlier ones beginning as far back in the sequence as magnesium protoporphyrin, may proceed via protein-bound intermediates. Pigment synthesis is probably closely interwoven with the formation of the cell organelles (e.g., chloroplasts and chromatophores) in which they are localized. Also, the final stages of chlorophyll formation entail integration with the system responsible for synthesis of the phytol residue and with other lipid-forming systems, since all chlorophyll-containing organelles are rich in lipid. It is, therefore, not surprising that disruption of the internal organization of cho-rophyll-forming cells results in loss of biosynthetic activity.

CONTROL MECHANISMS

The remarkable way in which all forms of life can adjust syn-thesis of tetrapyrroles to meet the demands of the environment provides a striking example of control of a biosynthetic pathway. The information about the regulatory mechanisms is sparse and it is here that the most interesting future developments may lie.

Control by feedback inhibition may be an important factor but firm evidence for such mechanisms can come only when the en-zymes of the pathway have been purified sufficiently to enable their properties to be studied.

The effect of environment on the formation of the biosynthetic enzymes has been studied mostly in bacteria but the in vitro sys-tem devised for the study of ALA synthetase in cultures of liver cells has great possibilities for extending the work to animal tis-sues. Such tissue culture preparations may also be exploited for investigating hemoprotein synthesis and could lead to the devel-opment of cell-free systems.

The rate of operation of the tricarboxylic acid cycle may play a central role in regulating tetrapyrrole synthesis since this cycle is the major source of succinyl CoA in most tetrapyrrole-forming organisms. Knowledge of the concentration of succinyl CoA in the metabolic pool under different environmental conditions is needed and this aspect might be profitably followed by isotopic tech-niques.

There is always the temptation to think of the control of tetra-pyrrole synthesis in terms of mechanisms known to apply in other biosynthetic systems. Most of this information has come from studies of the synthesis of amino acids and nucleic derivatives by microorganisms. Although many of the problems in tetrapyrrole synthesis are similar in general terms (for instance, in the regula-tion of the supply of intermediates to prevent their wasteful over-production), there are several unique features. There is the prob-lem of integration of the synthesis of the specific protein with that of the prosthetic group in the case of the hemoproteins. In plants and photosynthetic bacteria the iron and magnesium branches of the pathway have to be kept in step so that the same cell can elab-orate a large excess of chlorophyll compared to the hemes and can exert an independent control over each branch. Also to be considered is the effect of the physical environment on tetrapyrrole synthesis, such as the oxygen tension, and, in the case of photosynthetic organisms, the light intensity. In seeking for control mechanisms in tetrapyrrole synthesis the possibility of entirely novel principles must be constantly kept in mind.

BIOLOGICAL DECOMPOSITION OF TETRAPYRROLES

For the continuation of life on earth it is essential that organic material formed by living creatures be degraded to simple compounds upon death so that the cycles of carbon and nitrogen are maintained. Clearly there are mechanisms for the disposal of tetrapyrroles when animals and plants die, since hemes and chlorophylls are found only in living matter and do not occur, for instance, in the soil. Nor are there accumulations of expected decomposition products such as bile pigments and porphyrins.

Destruction of hemoglobin occurs in the living animal, the heme moiety being decomposed to bile pigments which are excreted in the urine and feces. The fate of the pigments after they have left the animal body is a complete mystery. It must be presumed that microorganisms in the soil and sewage are responsible for the destruction of the pyrrole rings. Organisms with the capacity to metabolize bile pigments or tetrapyrroles have not yet been described. An active search could be made for them by setting up enrichment cultures containing these pigments as sole nitrogen and carbon source; sewage is an obvious natural habitat for such organisms.

Chlorophyll breakdown occurs in living plants as shown by the yellowing of leaves when placed in the dark or as they age. The cleavage of the phytol ester group is presumably catalyzed by chlorophyllase. Subsequent photodecomposition of the liberated chlorophyllide to unknown products may ensue. As vegetable matter decays in the soil, chlorophyll degradation products are presumably attacked by microorganisms but nothing is known of these processes. Another site of microbial decomposition of chlorophyll derivatives is in the gut of herbivorous animals.

It seems likely that microorganisms have the last word in the biocomposition of tetrapyrroles, and this field offers challenging opportunities to the biochemist.

REFERENCES

Abel, K., N. Bauer, and J. T. Spence (1963), *Arch. Biochem. Biophys.*, **100**, 339.

Abrams, R. A., A. M. Altschul, and T. R. Hogness (1942), *J. Biol. Chem.*, **142**, 303.

Anderson, A. F. H. and M. Calvin (1962), *Nature*, **194**, 285.

Appleby, C. A. (1962), *Biochim. Biophys. Acta*, **60**, 226.

Arnon, D. I. (1963), in Symposium No. 6, *Proc. Intern. Congr. Biochem.*, *5th Moscow, 1961*, Pergamon, Oxford, p. 201.

Aronoff, S. (1960), in W. Ruhland (ed.), *Encyclopedia of Plant Physiology*, Vol. V/1, Springer-Verlag, Berlin, p. 234.

Barker, H. A. (1961), *Federation Proc.*, **20**, 956.

Barrett, J. (1956), *Biochem. J.*, **64**, 626.

Barrett, J. (1962), M. Sc. Thesis, University of New South Wales.

Bartsch, R. G. and M. D. Kamen (1958), *J. Biol. Chem.*, **230**, 41.

Bartsch, R. G. and M. D. Kamen (1960), *J. Biol. Chem.*, **235**, 825.

Bassham, J. A. and M. Calvin (1957), *The Path of Carbon in Photosynthesis*, Prentice-Hall, Englewood Cliffs, N.J.

Beljanski, M. and M. Beljanski (1957), *Ann. Inst. Pasteur*, **92**, 396.

Bergeron, J. A. (1959), *Brookhaven Symp. Biol.*, **11**, 118.

Bergersen, F. J. (1960), *Bacteriol. Rev.*, **24**, 246.

Bergersen, F. J. and M. J. Briggs (1958), *J. Gen. Microbiol.*, **19**, 482.

Bergerson, F. J. and P. W. Wilson (1959), *Proc. Natl. Acad. Sci. (U.S.),* **45,** 1641.

Bloch, K. and D. Rittenberg (1945), *J. Biol. Chem.,* **159,** 45.

Bogorad, L. (1958a), *J. Biol. Chem.,* **233,** 501.

Bogorad, L. (1958b), *J. Biol. Chem.,* **233,** 510.

Bogorad, L. (1958c), *J. Biol. Chem.,* **233,** 516.

Bogorad, L. (1962), in R. A. Lewin (ed.), *Physiology and Biochemistry of Algae,* Academic, New York, p. 385.

Bogorad, L. (1963), *Ann. N.Y. Acad. Sci.,* **104,** 676.

Bogorad, L. and S. Granick (1953a), *J. Biol. Chem.,* **202,** 793.

Bogorad, L. and S. Granick (1953b), *Proc. Natl. Acad. Sci. (U.S.),* **39,** 1176.

Bogorad, L. and A. B. Jacobson (1964), *Biochem. Biophys. Res. Commun.,* **14,** 113.

Bogorad, L. and G. S. Marks (1960), *J. Biol. Chem.,* **235,** 2127.

Bogorad, L., G. Pires, H. Swift, and W. J. McIlrath (1959), *Brookhaven Symp. Biol.,* **11,** 132.

Brawerman, G. (1963), *Biochim. Biophys. Acta,* **72,** 317.

Brawerman, G. and E. Chargaff (1959a), *Biochim. Biophys. Acta,* **31,** 164.

Brawerman, G. and E. Chargaff (1959b), *Biochim. Biophys. Acta,* **31,** 172.

Brawerman, G., A. O. Pogo, and E. Chargaff (1962), *Biochim. Biophys. Acta,* **55,** 326.

Bray, R. C. and D. Shemin (1963), *J. Biol. Chem.,* **238,** 1501.

Brown, E. G. (1958), *Nature,* **182,** 313.

Brown, G. M. and J. J. Reynolds (1963), *Ann. Rev. Biochem.,* **32,** 419.

Bruemmer, J. H., P. W. Wilson, J. L. Glenn, and F. L. Crane (1957), *J. Bacteriol.,* **73,** 113.

Bryant, M. P. and I. M. Robinson (1962), *J. Bacteriol.,* **84,** 605.

Bull, M. J. and J. Lascelles (1963), *Biochem. J.,* **87,** 15.

Burnham, B. F. (1962), *Arch. Biochem. Biophys.,* **97,** 329.

Burnham, B. F. (1963), *J. Gen. Microbiol.,* **32,** 117.

Burnham, B. F. and J. Lascelles (1963), *Biochem. J.,* **87,** 462.

Burnham, B. F. and J. B. Neilands (1961), *J. Biol. Chem.,* **236,** 554.

Calvin, M. (1959), *Brookhaven Symp. Biol.,* **11,** 160.

Carter, C. W., R. G. Macfarlane, J. R. P. O'Brien, and A. H. T. Robb-Smith (1945), *Biochem. J.,* **39,** 339.

Chance, B. (1954), *Science,* **120,** 767.

Chang, J. P. (1963), D. Phil. Thesis, University of Oxford.

Chang, J. P. and J. Lascelles (1963), *Biochem. J.,* **89,** 503.

Chantrenne, H. (1954), *Biochim. Biophys. Acta,* **14,** 157.

Chapman, J. A. and M. R. J. Salton (1962), *Arch. Mikrobiol.,* **44,** 311.

Chick, H., T. F. Macrae, A. J. P. Martin, and C. J. Martin (1938), *Biochem. J.,* **32,** 2207.

Clayton, R. K. (1959), *Arch. Mikrobiol.,* **33,** 260.

Clayton, R. K. (1960), *J. Biol. Chem.,* **235,** 405.

Clayton, R. K. and C. Smith (1960), *Biochem. Biophys. Res. Commun.,* **3,** 143.

Cohen-Bazire, G. and R. Kunisawa (1963), *J. Cell. Biol.*, **16**, 401.

Cohen-Bazire, G., W. R. Sistrom, and R. Y. Stanier (1957), *J. Cellular Comp. Physiol.*, **49**, 25.

Cookson, G. H. and C. Rimington (1954), *Biochem. J.*, **57**, 476.

Cooper, R. (1963), *Biochem. J.*, **89**, 100.

Cormier, M. J. and H. H. Rostorfer (1956), *Biochim. Biophys. Acta*, **22**, 229.

Daniel, J. W., J. Kelley, and H. P. Rusch (1962), *J. Bacteriol.*, **84**, 1104.

Davenport, H. E. and R. Hill (1952), *Proc. Roy. Soc. (London)*, **Ser B, 139,** 327.

Davies, D. D. (1959), *Biol. Rev. Cambridge Phil. Soc.*, **34**, 407.

Della Rosa, R. J., K. I. Altman, and K. Salomon (1953), *J. Biol. Chem.*, **202**, 771.

Dixon, M. and E. C. Webb (1964), *Enzymes*, Longmans, Green, London.

Dolin, M. I. (1961), in I. C. Gunsalus and R. Y. Stanier (eds.), *The Bacteria*, Vol. II, Academic, New York, p. 425.

Drabkin, D. L. (1951), *Physiol. Rev.*, **31**, 345.

Dresel, E. I. B. and J. E. Falk (1954), *Biochem. J.*, **56**, 156.

Dresel, E. I. B. and J. E. Falk (1956), *Biochem. J.*, **63**, 80.

Eilam, Y. and S. Klein (1962), *J. Cell. Biol.*, **14**, 169.

Eimhjellen, K. E., O. Aasmundrud, and A. Jensen (1963), *Biochem. Biophys. Res. Commun.*, **10**, 232.

Ellfolk, N. (1960), *Acta Chem. Scand.*, **14**, 1819.

Emery, T. and J..B. Neilands (1961), *J. Am. Chem. Soc.*, **83**, 1626.

Englesberg, E., J. B. Levy, and A. Gibor (1954), *J. Bacteriol.*, **68**, 178.

Ephrussi, B. (1952), *Harvey Lectures*, Ser 46, 45.

Eriksen, L. (1955), in G. E. W. Wolstenholme and E. C. P. Millar (eds.), *Ciba Foundation Symposium on Porphyrin Biosynthesis and Metabolism*, Churchill, London, p. 185.

Falk, J. E. (1954), *Biochem. Soc. Symp. (Cambridge, Eng.)*, **12**, 17.

Falk, J. E. (1961), *J. Chromatog.*, **5**, 277.

Falk, J. E. (1963), in M. Florkin and E. H. Stotz (eds.), *Comprehensive Biochemistry*, Vol. IX, Elsevier, Amsterdam, p. 3.

Falk, J. E. (1964), *Porphyrins and Metalloporphyrins*, Elsevier, Amsterdam.

Falk, J. E., E. I. B. Dresel, and C. Rimington (1953), *Nature*, **172**, 292.

Falk, J. E., R. Lemberg, and R. K. Morton (1961) (eds.), *Hematin Enzymes*, Pergamon, Oxford.

Falk, J. E., and R. J. Porra (1963), *Biochem. J.*, **90**, 66.

Falk, J. E., R. J. Porra, A. Brown, F. Moss, and H. E. Larminie (1959), *Nature*, **184**, 1217.

Fischer, F. G. and H. Bohn (1957), *Ann. Chem.*, **611**, 224.

Fox, H. M. (1947), *Proc. Roy. Soc. (London)*, Ser B 135, 195.

Fox, H. M. (1955), *Proc. Roy. Soc. (London)*, Ser B, **143**, 203.

French, C. S. (1960), in W. Ruhland (ed.), *Encyclopedia of Plant Physiology*, Vol. V/1, Springer-Verlag, Berlin, p. 252.

Galton, D. A. G. (1959), *Brit. Med. Bull.*, **15**, No. 1.

Gardner, J. E. and J. Lascelles (1962), *J. Gen. Microbiol.*, **29**, 157.

Geller, D. M. (1962), *J. Biol. Chem.*, **237**, 2947.

Gibson, J. (1961), *Biochem. J.*, **79**, 151.

Gibson, K. D. (1958), *Biochim. Biophys. Acta*, **28**, 451.

Gibson, K. D., W. G. Laver, and A. Neuberger (1958), *Biochem. J.*, **70**, 71.

Gibson, K. D., A. Neuberger, and J. J. Scott (1955), *Biochem. J.*, **61**, 618.

Gibson, K. D., A. Neuberger, and G. H. Tait (1962), *Biochem. J.*, **83**, 550.

Gibson, K. D., A. Neuberger, and G. H. Tait (1963), *Biochem. J.*, **88**, 325.

Giesbrecht, P. and G. Drews (1962), *Arch. Mikrobiol.*, **43**, 152.

Goldberg, A. and C. Rimington (1962), *Diseases of Porphyrin Metabolism*, Charles C Thomas, Springfield, Ill.

Goldberger, R., A. L. Smith, H. Tisdale, and R. Bomstein (1961), *J. Biol. Chem.*, **236**, 2788.

Gordon, H. S. (1959), *Physiol. Rev.*, **39**, 1.

Granick, S. (1948a), *J. Biol. Chem.*, **172**, 717.

Granick, S. (1948b), *J. Biol. Chem.*, **175**, 333.

Granick, S. (1950a), *Harvey Lectures*, **44**, 220.

Granick, S. (1950b), *J. Biol. Chem.*, **183**, 713.

Granick, S. (1954), *Science*, **120**, 1105.

Granick, S. (1961a), in J. Brachet and A. G. Mirsky (eds.), *The Cell*, Vol. II, Academic, New York, p. 489.

Granick, S. (1961b), *J. Biol. Chem.*, **236**, 1168.

Granick, S. (1962), *Trans. N.Y. Acad. Sci.*, **25**, 53.

Granick, S. (1963a), in Symposium No. 6, *Proc. Intern. Congr. Biochem., 5th, Moscow, 1961*, Pergamon, Oxford, p. 176.

Granick, S. (1963b), in M. Locke (ed.), *Cytodifferential and Macromolecular Synthesis*, Academic, New York, p. 144.

Granick, S. (1963c), *J. Biol. Chem.*, **238**, PC2247.

Granick, S., L. Bogorad, and H. Jaffe (1953), *J. Biol. Chem.*, **202**, 801.

Granick, S. and H. Gilder (1947), *Advan. Enzymol.*, **7**, 305.

Granick, S. and D. Mauzerall (1958), *J. Biol. Chem.*, **232**, 1119.

Granick, S. and D. Mauzerall (1961), in D. M. Greenberg (ed.), *Metabolic Pathways*, Vol. II, Academic, New York, p. 525.

Granick, S. and G. Urata (1963), *J. Biol. Chem.*, **238**, 821.

Granick, S. and H. G. Vanden Schrieck (1955), *Proc. Soc. Exp. Biol. Med.*, **88**, 270.

Grassl, M., U. Coy, R. Seyffert, and F. Lynen (1963), *Biochem. Z.*, **338**, 771.

Gray, C. H. (1961), *Bile Pigments in Health and Disease*, Charles C Thomas, Springfield, Ill.

Green, D. E. (1963), *Comp. Biochem. Physiol.*, **4**, 81.

Green, M., K. I. Altman, J. E. Richmond, and K. Salomon (1957), *Nature*, **179**, 375.

Greenberg, D. M. (1961), in D. M. Greenberg (ed.), *Metabolic Pathways*, Vol. II, Academic, New York, p. 173.

Greengard, C. and P. Feigelson (1962), *J. Biol. Chem.*, **237**, 1903.

Griffiths, D. E. and D. C. Wharton (1961), *J. Biol. Chem.*, **236**, 1850.

Griffiths, M. (1962), *J. Gen. Microbiol.*, **27**, 427.

Hager, L. P. (1962), in P. D. Boyer, H. Lardy, and K. Myrbäck (eds.), *The Enzymes*, Vol. VI, Academic, New York, p. 387.

Hamilton, P. B., A. L. Shug, and P. W. Wilson (1957), *Proc. Natl. Acad. Sci. (U.S.)*, **43**, 297.

Hartree, E. F. (1957), *Advan. Enzymol.*, **18**, 1.

Hayaishi, O. (1963) (ed.), *The Oxygenases*, Academic, New York.

Heinrich, H. C. (1963) (ed.), *2te Europäisches Symposium über B$_{12}$ und Intrinsic Factor*, Ferdinand Enke Verlag, Stuttgart.

Herbert, D. and J. Pinsent (1948), *Biochem. J.*, **43**, 193.

Hickman, D. D. and A. W. Frenkel (1959), *J. Biophys. Biochem. Cytol.*, **6**, 277.

Hill, R. (1963), in M. Florkin and E. H. Stotz (eds.), *Comprehensive Biochemistry*, Vol. IX, Elsevier, Amsterdam, p. 73.

Hill, R. and R. Scarisbrick (1951), *New Phytologist*, **50**, 98.

Hernandez, H. H. and I. L. Chaikoff (1957), *J. Biol. Chem.*, **228**, 447.

Hoare, D. B. and H. Heath (1959), *Biochem. J.*, **73**, 679.

Holden, M. (1961), *Biochem. J.*, **78**, 359.

Holt, A. S. and H. V. Morley (1959), *Can. J. Chem.*, **37**, 507.

Holt, A. S., D. W. Hughes, H. J. Kende, and J. W. Purdie (1962), *J. Am. Chem. Soc.*, **84**, 2835.

Holt, A. S., D. W. Hughes, H. J. Kende, and T. W. Purdie (1963), *Pl. Cell Physiol. (Tokyo)*, **4**, 49.

Huennekens, F. M. and B. W. Gabrio (1954), *Federation Proc.*, **13**, 232.

Hutcher, F. H. and S. F. Conti (1960), *Biochem. Biophys. Res. Commun.*, **3**, 497.

Ingram, V. M. (1961), *Hemoglobin and its Abnormalities*, Charles C Thomas, Springfield, Ill.

Jacobs, N. J. and M. J. Wolin (1963a), *Biochim. Biophys. Acta*, **69**, 18.

Jacobs, N. J. and M. J. Wolin (1963b), *Biochim. Biophys. Acta*, **69**, 29.

Jensen, J. (1957), *J. Bacteriol.*, **73**, 324.

Jensen, J. (1962), *Biochem. Biophys. Res. Commun.*, **8**, 271.

Jensen, J. and E. Thofern (1953), *Z. Naturforsch.*, **8b**, 599.

Jones, O. T. G. (1963a), *Biochem. J.*, **86**, 429.

Jones, O. T. G. (1963b), *Biochem. J.*, **88**, 335.

Jones, O. T. G. (1963c), *Biochem. J.*, **89**, 182.

Jones, O. T. G. (1964), *Biochem. J.*, **91**, 572.

Jørgensen, S. K. and T. K. With (1955), *Nature*, **176**, 156.

Jørgensen, S. K. and T. K. With (1963), *Ann. N.Y. Acad. Sci.*, **104**, 701.

Jukes, T. H. (1953), in G. H. Bourne and G. W. Kidder (eds.), *Biochemistry and Physiology of Nutrition*, Vol. I, Academic, New York, p. 328.

Kamen, M. D. (1963), in Symposium No. 6, *Proc. Intern. Congr. Biochem., 5th, Moscow, 1961*, Pergamon, Oxford, p. 242.

Kamen, M. D. and R. G. Bartsch (1961), in J. E. Falk, R. Lemberg, and R. K. Morton (eds.), *Hematin Enzymes*, Vol. II, Pergamon, Oxford, p. 419.

Keilin, D. (1953), *Nature*, **172**, 390.

Keilin, D. and E. F. Hartree (1945), *Biochem. J.*, **39**, 293.

Keilin, D. and J. F. Ryley (1953), *Nature*, **172**, 451.

Keilin, D. and J. D. Smith (1947), *Nature*, **159**, 692.

Keilin, D. and A. Tissières (1953), *Nature*, **172**, 393.

Keilin, D. and Y. L. Wang (1945), *Nature*, **155**, 227.

Keister, D. L., A. T. Jagendorf, and A. San Pietro (1962), *Biochim. Biophys. Acta*, **62**, 332.

Kennedy, E. P. (1961), *Federation Proc.*, **20**, 934.

Kikuchi, G., A. Kumar, and D. Shemin (1959), *Federation Proc.*, **18**, 259.

Kikuchi, G., A. Kumar, P. Talmage, and D. Shemin (1958), *J. Biol. Chem.*, **233**, 1214.

Klein, S. (1962), *Nature*, **196**, 992.

Klein, A. O. and W. Vishniac (1961), *J. Biol. Chem.*, **236**, 2544.

Kornberg, H. L. (1959), *Ann. Rev. Microbiol.*, **13**, 49.

Kranz, S. B., O. Gallien-Lartigue, and E. Goldwasser (1963), *J. Biol. Chem.*, **238**, 4085.

Krebs, H. A. and J. M. Lowenstein (1960), in D. M. Greenberg (ed.), *Metabolic Pathways*, Vol. I, Academic, New York, p. 129.

Kupke, D. W. (1962), *J. Biol. Chem.*, **237**, 3287.

Kupke, D. W. and C. S. French (1960), in W. Ruhland (ed.), *Encyclopedia of Plant Physiology*, Vol. V/1, Springer-Verlag, Berlin, p. 298.

Labbe, R. F. and N. Hubbard (1960), *Biochim. Biophys. Acta*, **41**, 185.

Labbe, R. F. and N. Hubbard (1961), *Biochim. Biophys. Acta*, **52**, 130.

Labbe, R. F., N. Hubbard, and N. S. Caughey (1963), *Biochemistry*, **2**, 372.

Lascelles, J. (1956a), *Biochem. J.*, **62**, 78.

Lascelles, J. (1956b), *J. Gen. Microbiol.*, **15**, 404.

Lascelles, J. (1957), *Biochem. J.*, **66**, 65.

Lascelles, J. (1959), *Biochem. J.*, **72**, 508.

Lascelles, J. (1960), *J. Gen. Microbiol.*, **23**, 487.

Lascelles, J. (1962a), *J. Gen. Microbiol.*, **29**, 47.

Lascelles, J. (1962b), in I. C. Gunsalus and R. Y. Stanier (eds.), *The Bacteria*, Vol. III, Academic, New York, p. 335.

Lascelles, J. (1963), in L. P. Vernon (ed.), *Symposium on Bacterial Photosynthesis*, Antioch Press, Yellow Springs, Ohio.

Laver, W. G., A. Neuberger, and S. Udenfriend (1958), *Biochem. J.*, **70**, 4.

Lemberg, R. and J. W. Legge (1949), *Hematin Compounds and Bile Pigments*, Wiley-Interscience, New York.

Lemberg, R., P. Clezy, and J. Barrett (1961), in J. E. Falk, R. Lemberg, and R. K. Morton (eds.), *Hematin Enzymes*, Vol. I, Pergamon, Oxford, p. 344.

Lenhoff, H. M. and N. O. Kaplan (1956), *J. Biol. Chem.*, **220**, 967.

Lenhoff, H. M., D. J. D. Nicholas, and N. O. Kaplan (1956), *J. Biol. Chem.*, **220**, 983.

Linnane, A. W., E. Vitols, and P. G. Nowland (1962), *J. Cell. Biol.*, **13**, 345.

Lockwood, W. H. and A. Benson (1960), *Biochem. J.*, **75**, 372.

London, I. M. (1961), *Harvey Lectures,* **56,** 151.

London, I. M., D. Shemin, and D. Rittenberg (1949), *J. Biol. Chem.,* **173,** 797.

London, I. M., D. Shemin, and D. Rittenberg (1950), *J. Biol. Chem.,* **183,** 749.

Lyttleton, J. W., and P. O. P. Ts'o (1958), *Arch. Biochem. Biophys.,* **73,** 120.

Margulies, M. M. (1962), *Plant Physiol.,* **37,** 473.

Marr, A. G. (1960), in I. C. Gunsalus and R. Y. Stanier (eds.), *The Bacteria,* Vol. I, Academic, New York, p. 443.

Marsh, H. W., H. J. Evans, and G. Matrone (1963a), *Plant Physiol.,* **38,** 632.

Marsh, H. W., H. J. Evans, and G. Matrone (1963b), *Plant Physiol.,* **38,** 638.

Marsh, J. B. and D. L. Drabkin (1957), *J. Biol. Chem.,* **224,** 909.

Mauzerall, D. and S. Granick (1956), *J. Biol. Chem.,* **219,** 435.

Mauzerall, D. and S. Granick (1958), *J. Biol. Chem.,* **232,** 1141.

Mego, J. L. and A. T. Jagendorf (1961), *Biochim. Biophys. Acta,* **53,** 237.

Morell, H., J. C. Savoie, and I. M. London (1958), *J. Biol. Chem.,* **233,** 923.

Morton, R. K. (1958), *Rev. Pure Appl. Chem.,* **8,** 161.

Moss., F. O. (1956). *Australian J. Exp. Biol. Med. Sci.,* **34,** 395.

Moyed, H. S. and H. E. Umbarger (1962), *Physiol. Rev.,* **42,** 444.

Mühlethaler, K. and A. Frey-Wyssling (1959), *J. Biophys. Biochem. Cytol.,* **6,** 507.

Muir, H. M. and A. Neuberger (1950), *Biochem. J.,* **47,** 97.

Musilek, V. (1962), *Science,* **137,** 674.

Neilands, J. B. (1957), *Bacteriol. Rev.,* **21,** 101.

Neuberger, A. and J. J. Scott (1953), *Nature,* **172,** 1093.

Neve, R. A., R. F. Labbe, and R. A. Aldrich (1956), *J. Am. Chem. Soc.,* **78,** 691.

Newton, J. W. and M. D. Kamen (1961), in I. C. Gunsalus and R. Y. Stanier (eds.), *The Bacteria,* Vol. II, Academic, New York, p. 397.

Nishida, G. and R. F. Labbe (1959), *Biochim. Biophys. Acta,* **31,** 519.

Nishimura, M. and B. Chance (1963), *Biochim. Biophys. Acta,* **66,** 1.

ÓhEocha, C. (1962), in R. A. Lewin (ed.), *Physiology and Biochemistry of Algae,* Academic, New York, p. 421.

Onisawa, J. and R. F. Labbe (1963), *Science,* **140,** 1326.

Pappenheimer, A. M. (1947), *J. Biol. Chem.,* **167,** 251.

Pappenheimer, A. M. (1955), in S. P. Colowick and N. O. Kaplan (eds.), *Methods in Enzymology,* Vol II, Academic, New York, p. 744.

Pappenheimer, A. M. and E. D. Hendee (1947), *J. Biol. Chem.,* **171,** 701.

Paul, K. G. (1960), in P. D. Boyer, H. Lardy, and K. M. Myrbäck (eds.), *The Enzymes,* Vol. III, Academic, New York, p. 277.

Perur, N. G., R. L. Smith, and H. H. Wiebe (1961), *Plant Physiol.,* **36,** 736.

Perutz, M. F. (1962), *Proteins and Nucleic Acids,* Elsevier, Amsterdam.

Phillips, J. N. (1963), in M. Florkin and E. H. Stotz (eds.), *Comprehensive Biochemistry,* Vol. IX, Elsevier, Amsterdam, p. 34.

Pizer, L. I. (1963), *J. Biol. Chem.,* **238,** 3934.

Popják, G. and J. W. Cornforth (1960), *Advan. Enzymol.,* **22,** 281.

Porra, R. J. and J. E. Falk (1963), *Biochem. J.,* **90,** 69.

Porra, R. J. and D. T. G. Jones (1963), *Biochem. J.*, **87**, 186.

Postgate, J. R. (1956), *J. Gen. Microbiol.*, **14**, 545.

Postgate, J. R. (1959), *Ann. Rev. Microbiol.*, **13**, 505.

Postgate, J. R. (1961), in J. E. Falk, R. Lemberg, and R. K. Morton (eds.), *Hematin Enzymes*, Vol. II, Pergamon, Oxford, p. 407.

Rabinowitch, E. I. (1945, 1951, 1956), *Photosynthesis and Related Processes*, Vols. 1, 2, 3, Wiley-Interscience, New York.

Rapoport, H. and H. P. Hamlow (1961), *Biochem. Biophys. Res. Commun.*, **6**, 134.

Rimington, C. and G. J. Kennedy (1962), in M. Florkin and H. S. Mason (eds.), *Comparative Biochemistry*, Vol. IV, Academic, New York, p. 557.

Sager, R. (1959), *Brookhaven Symp. Biol.*, **11**, 101.

Sano, S. and S. Granick (1961), *J. Biol. Chem.*, **236**, 1173.

Schachman, H. K., A. B. Pardee, and R. Y. Stanier (1952), *Arch. Biochem. Biophys.*, **38**, 245.

Schaeffer, P. (1952), *Biochim. Biophys. Acta*, **9**, 261.

Schatz, G. (1963), *Biochem. Biophys. Res. Commun.*, **12**, 448.

Schatz, G., H. Tuppy, and J. Klima (1963), *Z. Naturforsch.*, **18b**, 145.

Schmid, R., J. F. Figen, and S. Schwartz (1955), *J. Biol. Chem.*, **217**, 263.

Schmid, R. and S. Schwarz (1955), in G. E. W. Wolstenholme and E. C. P. Millar (eds.), *Ciba Foundation Symposium on Porphyrin Biosynthesis and Metabolism*, Churchill, London, p. 196.

Schroeder, W. A. (1963), *Ann. Rev. Biochem.*, **32**, 301.

Schulman, M. P. and D. A. Richert (1957), *J. Biol. Chem.*, **226**, 181.

Schumm, O. (1927), *Die Spektrochemische Analyse Naturlichen Organischer Farbstoffe*, Fischer, Jena.

Schwarz, S. and H. M. Wikoff (1952), *J. Biol. Chem.*, **194**, 563.

Schwarz, H. G., R. Goudsmit, R. L. Hill, G. E. Cartwright, and M. M. Wintrobe (1961), *J. Clin. Invest.*, **40**, 188.

Šesták, Z. (1958), *J. Chromatog.*, **1**, 293.

Shemin, D. (1955a), in W. D. McElroy and H. B. Glass (eds.), *Amino Acid Metabolism*, Johns Hopkins Press, Baltimore, p. 727.

Shemin, D. (1955b), in G. E. W. Wolstenholme and E. C. P. Millar (eds.), *Ciba Foundation Symposium on Porphyrin Biosynthesis and Metabolism*, Churchill, London, p. 4.

Shemin, D. and S. Kumin (1952), *J. Biol. Chem.*, **198**, 827.

Shemin, D. and D. Rittenberg (1946), *J. Biol. Chem.*, **166**, 621.

Shemin, D. and C. S. Russell (1953), *J. Am. Chem. Soc.*, **75**, 4873.

Shemin, D., C. S. Russell, and T. Abramsky (1955), *J. Biol. Chem.*, **215**, 613.

Shemin, D. and J. Wittenberg (1951), *J. Biol. Chem.*, **192**, 315.

Shimizo, S. and E. Tamaki (1963), *Arch. Biochem. Biophys.*, **102**, 152.

Simpson, M. V. (1962), *Ann. Rev. Biochem.*, **31**, 333.

Sistrom, W. R., M. Griffiths, and R. Y. Stanier (1956), *J. Cellular Comp. Physiol.*, **48**, 459.

Slonimski, P. P. (1953), *La Formation des Enzymes Respiratoires chez la Levure*, Masson, Paris.

Slonimski, P. P. (1956), in "Conférence et Rapports," *Proc. Intern. Congr. Biochem., 3rd, Brussels, 1955*, Vaillant-Catmanne, Liège, p. 242.

Smillie, R. M. (1963), *Can. J. Botany*, **41**, 123.

Smith, E. Lester (1960), *Vitamin B_{12}*, Methuen, London.

Smith, J. D. (1949a), *Biochem. J.*, **44**, 585.

Smith, J. D. (1949b), *Biochem. J.* **44**, 591.

Smith, J. H. C. (1960), in M. B. Allen (ed.), *Comparative Biochemistry of Photoreactive Systems*, Academic, New York, p. 257.

Smith, J. H. C. (1961), in T. W. Goodwin and O. Lindberg (eds.), *Biological Structure and Function*, Vol. II, Academic, New York, p. 325.

Smith, J. H. C. (1963), in Symposium No. 6, *Proc. Intern. Congr. Biochem., 5th, Moscow, 1961*, Pergamon, Oxford, p. 151.

Smith, J. H. C. and A. Benitez (1955), in K. Paech and M. V. Tracey (eds.), *Modern Methods of Plant Analysis*, Vol. IV, Springer-Verlag, Berlin, p. 142.

Smith, L. (1954), *Arch. Biochem. Biophys.*, **50**, 299.

Smith, L. (1961), in I. C. Gunsalus and R. Y. Stanier (eds.), *The Bacteria*, Vol. II, Academic, New York, p. 365.

Smith, L. and M. Baltscheffsky (1959), *J. Biol. Chem.*, **234**, 1575.

Smith, L. and B. Chance (1958), *Ann. Rev. Plant Physiol.*, **9**, 449.

Smith, J. H. C. and C. S. French (1963), *Ann. Rev. Plant Physiol.*, **14**, 181.

Smith, M. H., P. George, and J. R. Preer (1962), *Arch. Biochem. Biophys.*, **99**, 313.

Stadtman, E. R. (1963), *Bacteriol. Rev.*, **27**, 170.

Stadtman, T. C. (1960), *J. Bacteriol.*, **79**, 904.

Stanier, R. Y. and G. Cohen-Bazire (1957), in R. E. O. Williams and C. C. Spicer (eds.), *Microbial Ecology*, Cambridge University Press, Cambridge, p. 56.

Stanier, R. Y. and J. H. C. Smith (1959), *Carnegie Inst. of Wash. Year Book*, **58**, 336.

Stern, J. R. (1963), *Biochim. Biophys. Acta*, **69**, 435.

Sugita, Y. (1962), *J. Biochem. (Tokyo)*, **51**, 436.

Sugita, Y., Y. Yoneyama, and H. Ohyama (1962), *J. Biochem. (Tokyo)*, **51**, 450.

Tanaka, T. and W. E. Knox (1959), *J. Biol. Chem.*, **234**, 1162.

Thofern, E. (1961), *Ergebn. Mikrobiol.*, **34**, 213.

Tissières, A. and H. K. Mitchell (1954), *J. Biol. Chem.*, **208**, 241.

Tokuyama, K. and W. E. Knox (1964), *Biochim. Biophys. Acta*, **81**, 201.

Tuttle, A. L. and H. Gest (1959), *Proc. Natl. Acad. Sci. (U.S.)*, **45**, 1261.

Umbarger, E. and B. D. Davis (1962), in I. C. Gunsalus and R. Y. Stanier (eds.), *The Bacteria*, Vol. III, Academic, New York, p. 167.

Umbarger, H. E., M. A. Umbarger, and P. M. L. Siu (1963), *J. Bacteriol.*, **85**, 1431.

Urata, G. and S. Granick (1963), *J. Biol. Chem.*, **238**, 811.

Van Niel, C. B. (1944), *Bacteriol. Rev.*, **8**, 1.

Vatter, A. E., H. C. Douglas, and R. S. Wolfe (1959), *J. Bacteriol.*, **77**, 812.

Verhoeven, W. and Y. Takeda (1956), in W. D. McElroy and H. B. Glass (eds.), *Inorganic Nitrogen Metabolism*, Johns Hopkins Press, Baltimore, p. 159.

Vernon, L. P. and M. D. Kamen (1954), *J. Biol. Chem.*, **211**, 643.

Vogel, W., D. A. Richert, B. Q. Pixley, and M. P. Schulman (1960), *J. Biol. Chem.*, **235**, 1769.

Wang, L. C., J. Garcia-Rivera, and R. H. Burris (1961), *Biochem. J.*, **81**, 237.

Weibull, C. (1953), *J. Bacteriol.*, **66**, 696.

Westall, R. G. (1952), *Nature*, **170**, 614.

White, D. C. (1962), *J. Bacteriol.*, **83**, 851.

White, D. C., M. P. Bryant, and D. R. Caldwell (1962), *J. Bacteriol.*, **84**, 822.

White, D. C. and S. Granick (1963), *J. Bacteriol.*, **85**, 842.

Willstätter, R. and M. Mieg (1913), *Ann. Chem*, **400**, 147.

Wimpenny, J. W. T., M. Ranlett, and C. T. Gray (1963), *Biochim. Biophys. Acta*, **73**, 170.

Wintrobe, M. M. (1961), *Clinical Hematology*, Henry Kimpton, London.

Wittenberg, J. and D. Shemin (1949), *J. Biol. Chem.*, **178**, 47.

Wittenberg, J. and D. Shemin (1950), *J. Biol. Chem.*, **185**, 103.

Wolff, J. B. and L. Price (1957), *Arch. Biochem. Biophys.*, **72**, 293.

Wolken, J. J. (1961), in M. V. Edds (ed.), *Macromolecular Complexes*, Ronald, New York, p. 85.

Wriston, J. C., L. Lack, and D. Shemin (1955), *J. Biol. Chem.*, **215**, 603.

Yamanaka, T. and K. Okunuki (1963), *Biochim. Biophys. Acta*, **67**, 407.

Yamanaka, T. and K. Okunuki (1963), *Biochem. Z.*, **338**, 62.

Yčas, M. and D. L. Drabkin (1957), *J. Biol. Chem.*, **224**, 921.

Yoneyama, Y., H. Ohyama, Y. Sugita, and H. Yoshikawa (1962), *Biochim. Biophys. Acta*, **62**, 261.

Yoneyama, Y., H. Ohyama, Y. Sugita, and H. Yoshikawa (1963), *Biochim. Biophys. Acta*, **74**, 635.

Zähner, H., E. Bachmann, R. Hütter, and J. Nüesch (1962), *Pathol. Microbiol.*, **25**, 708.

INDEX

10/12/64 ~~